The Lady of Yaddo was small and frail, but she used the power of her pen, her purse and her principles to leave a large imprint on her world. She lived the life of a queen in her baronial estate Yaddo and moved with the well known and well connected of the Gilded Age, but when she saw a woman in need she called her "sister."

Katrina Trask's "memoir" is a reflection of the late Victorian era witnessing its glory and its demise in the exuberant and extravagant days of the Gilded Age. Her life in two summer colonies at the turn of the twentieth century was privileged, but she had questions; she lived as a Lady but sought to serve. Her memoir paints a life fashioned by high drama and deep sorrow, but one seeking relevance and purpose. Armed with steely grit, a sturdy faith, and her belief in the Power of Woman, the Lady of Yaddo, through this work of Lynn Esmay, shares her emotional memoir on a colorful landscape of American history. ✾

Lady of Yaddo

The Gilded Age Memoir of
Katrina Trask

╼ *by Lynn Esmay* ╾

French Mountain Press

2013

Published by French Mountain Press,
Diamond Point, New York, 2013

To order books: Publisher's website: LadyofYaddo.com

or

French Mountain Press
Box 111
Diamond Point, N.Y. 12824

ISBN Number 978-0-9884123-1-6

Edited by Jane Mackintosh.
Cover design and artwork by Arielle Landsberg,
Tone Creative, Saratoga Springs, N. Y.
Interior book design and artwork by Jane Mackintosh,
Queensbury, N. Y.

Printed in the United States of America

Front cover images:
Postcard of Yaddo courtesy of Victoria Garlanda,
Saratoga Room of Saratoga Springs Public Library;
portrait of young Katrina Trask courtesy of Saratoga
Springs History Museum.

Back cover image:
Gustave Lorey photo of Katrina's garden entrance,
courtesy of Jane Wait.

Acknowledgements

To my husband, who said "Yes you can."
Like Spencer, he had a way of making it happen.
And like Katrina, I knew he would.

To Teri Blasko and Victoria Garlanda whose knowledge, ideas, direction, and tireless energy in the Saratoga Room of the Saratoga Springs Public Library made working there a delightful experience.

To Tal Nadan, reference archivist in the Manuscript and Archives Division of the Brooke Russell Astor Reading Room of the New York Public Library, for her enthusiasm and assistance.

To those who helped me with photo acquisition: Yaddo Corporation; Jane Wait of the Yaddo Garden Association; Teri and Victoria in the Saratoga Springs Library; John Conners at the Saratoga Springs History Museum; Centennial editors of the Lake George Club's *Family of Friends;* Chris Dixon at Wiawaka Holiday House; Dusty and Nancy Rhodes of Clay Island; Pat and Dick Swire of Three Brother Island.

To friends who listened, read, critiqued, suggested, and supported me while I was "away someplace" working on the project, or not away but talking about it too much.

To Jane Mackintosh for her editing, helpful comments, patience, and encouragement. To Arielle Landsberg for the book cover and inviting web-site design.

To my daughter Kimberly Taylor who gave me fine legal advice, and my other children who inspired me with their confidence.

Spencer and Katrina Trask dancing the
minuet in period costumes at Yaddo, about 1899.
{ Courtesy Corporation of Yaddo }

Note from the Author

This work is fiction, but the story is told in
the voice of the real Lady of Yaddo, Katrina Trask,
as her memoir. The narrative often comes in Katrina's
own words, taken from the Trask correspondence
and records held in the Yaddo archives of the New
York Public Library and in the Saratoga Room of
the Saratoga Springs Public Library. These letters,
documents, and scrapbooks along with her own novels,
poems, and essays shape the literary style and the
views of the fictionalized Katrina. The author tries to
honor the spirit and the facts of her tumultuous life.

— Lynn Esmay
Diamond Point, Lake George, 2013

Post Script:
Extended italicized passages in the following text
reflect two things: direct quotations from the journals,
writings, or correspondence of Katrina Trask; or this
author's interpretation of Katrina's thoughts and words
— in which case quotation marks do not appear.

Portrait pictures of young Katrina and Spencer.
{ Courtesy Saratoga Springs History Museum }

Table of Contents

Katrina Trask at her desk.
{ Courtesy Saratoga Springs History Museum }

My Dear Reader

This was how it began, my personal journal, my continuing *Chronicles of Yaddo*. During the early spring-time of the Great Blizzard of 1888 an unspeakable tragedy occurred which happened in our city home in Brooklyn Heights, but it belongs to the story of Yaddo, because it forever changed my life... and it changed the life of our blessed country home up the Hudson in Saratoga Springs.

After the great loss, my husband and the children's nanny encouraged me to record my feelings. The catharsis of writing. And so I began, and continued throughout my life this personal diary of Katrina Trask and her Yaddo estate. It was not meant to be shared like my professional writing. It was a record of my unique pilgrimage for meaning and purposeful living, but perhaps it is, in fact, your journey, too.

For words, like Nature, half reveal
And half conceal the Soul within.

Yours with love,
Katrina Trask

Brooklyn Heights, New York, 1888

A serpent of death slithers past the ramshackle dwellings of the immigrants in Essex Street, past the windowless shirt factories, the rag pickers struggling with pushcarts against snow drifts in lower Manhattan. It ignores for now the hollow-eyed immigrant children from Poland and Russia huddled in the shadow of their tenement alley, scrapping over a lump of coal. It dodges the steamy dung of trolley horses, the garbage along the ditches, now purified and encased in soft curves of snow left from the blizzard. It is unaware of the crackling wires dangling from the electrical poles, the stalled traffic in the financial district. It is undaunted by the recent storm, making its way brazenly over the new Brooklyn Bridge into Willow Street in Brooklyn Heights, Willow Street, wide and beautiful and serene in whisper-soft magical snow.

It is a democratic beast, embracing the lowly and nameless newcomer as well as the mighty families of established old New York. It has invaded the throats of young and old, weaving a thick and suffocating membrane around tonsils and across throats to a hideous and agonizing end. The newest victim of this dreaded diphtheria is a lady of significance in Brooklyn Heights, the wife of well-known New York financier Spencer Trask. She is a woman of exceptional beauty and intelligence. The Trasks come from established genteel families of integrity and wealth. Now each is panoplied to do battle with the intruding monster poised to destroy their fairy-tale life.

Kate Nichols Trask languishes next to death in the neighborhood where old-moneyed New Yorkers made their homes. She lies in a dreamland of fever-wrought memories and thoughts. She is unaware of the timid kisses and grave faces of her little daughter and son by her bedside, the children finally allowed to say good-bye to Mama with Doctor's permission.

After all, it was thought, the time of contagion had passed. The children would be inured to the disease. Serious young Christina is her mother's clone in so many ways, a child quite at home in adult company and articulate and wise beyond her years. She is no stranger to illness and death: her older brother lies in the Greenwood Cemetery. She remembers a household shadowed by mourning only a few years ago. She is a mute statue by her mother's bedside, and she does not want another sad story in their lives. But this will, indeed, be another sad story.

Her little brother Spencer — she calls him Junius — barely able to reach his mother's face, will be the first to die from the diphtheria within days of this moment.

A few days later eleven-year old Christina herself will be laid out neatly on her bed, a still, cold angel, brought down ruthlessly from her buoyant days. The mother Kate is at this time too ill to realize that she, in fact, is destined to recover, and that her children will be victims of the same scourge ravaging the street children of immigrant families in lower Manhattan. What bitter irony for Kate to wake to a somber home after the joy in her own recovery. How difficult it will be for the Trasks, strong in spirit, positive by nature, to accept the injustice of their loss in that spring of 1888.

Spencer Trask speaks in a tremulous voice, not the voice of wise man of Wall Street, intrepid entrepreneur, master of indomitable will:

"Doctor Gibbons, I beg of you… at least let Christina and Spencer bid good-bye to their mama… she would beseech you, so gently, so eloquently, as only Kate would, and ask nothing more. They must see her one last time. No, no. You MUST."

The distraught man is a formidable figure standing at the window. Tall, elegant, of regal bearing with his square shoulders and neat beard, he has suddenly fallen to his knees at the feet of the doctor. Now his square shoulders are a sinking curve of desolation.

"How can there be NOTHING more to do? How can I suffer her loss? Has my God not exacted ENOUGH? We lost our first born son Alanson, Doctor Gibbons, before he was five. Kate suffers from heart issues, and yet she is the most vital woman I know, the kindest, the most generous, the most romantic soul. She has more talent and creativity than any woman I've ever met. She lights up the room with her beauty and grace, she brings compassion to her friends and to our servants, she charms diplomats and royalty with her wit and her insight, she writes poetry and plays. You should watch her match her wit with the brightest men at the dinner table. Kate is... she is Spencer's *fairy queen.*"

He is crying now, the wealthy financier who recently, with assurance, backed an untried idea of Thomas Edison and helped illuminate New York city. The man of railroads, of silver mining in the West, the man who invests wisely in New York real estate, who supports the art scene in New York, and who oversees his own prestigious investment banking firm. The man who is on a first name basis with the President and with John D. Rockefeller, Jay Gould, J. P. Morgan.

"We LOVE God, and we love our fellow man. We lead a privileged life, but we give generously, we act nobly, always for the betterment of mankind. Where is there justice, Doctor, please tell me? Hasn't God had enough?"

"Mr. Trask, Mr. Trask. These are questions for God alone. I am only a doctor. Life and death are mysteries to man. Mrs. Trask is comfortable, at least, but she is not cured. I only give you the truth so you can prepare yourself."

And then, after agonizing moments of heavy silence, his bearing recovered, a silent prayer mouthed, he wills himself to accept his fate. He discovers an inner strength of spiritual ballast more powerful than he had imagined. Spencer Trask comes from strong Puritan stock. His father Alanson Trask had bequeathed him a Christian humility as well as a belief in the courage of his convictions. The independent son had left the comfortable security of his uncle's firm to open his own investment company; he had amassed a material fortune, but like his father he has remained first a humble servant of his fellow man and of God. Much had been bestowed upon him in his young life: professional success, splendid fortune, elegant homes, beautiful wife, accomplished children. And now much is expected of him. He will harden his emotional shell and endure. For the children and for the Trask name. It was the right thing to do.

Prisoner of fever and fatigue, a body is captive, but a mind is loosed and can wander freely in time. Kate Trask, small and beautiful, looks weak and lost in her big bed. She is seemingly absent from the room. But without her caregivers' knowledge or awareness Kate is savoring all the bright moments of her young life, long before she was waylaid by diphtheria. For days now, she has escaped into her past and lives again among her friends and family in an earlier day. At this moment she is drifting through her own story, her childhood, her studies, her coming of age. She sees the Kate Nichols who was schooled at home by tutors, introduced to literature, French, the Bible, philosophy, history. She sees the girl small in stature but proud of her intellect, determined to keep up with her brothers who went to Brooklyn Polytechnic Institute, then Williams College, and Columbia Law School. Kate is aware of the effect of her beauty: the hypnotic blue eyes, the luxurious chestnut hair tied loosely behind her head, the fine posture, her challenging sexual appeal. She remembers riding in fine carriages, speaking politely with Papa's connected friends, trying on the latest silk fashions with Mama, and making her debut. But mostly she remembers the inward drive to make her intellectual landscape as captivating as her outward appearance. She strives to make her feminine position more dynamic in a strictly-drawn hierarchy of roles. Kate Nichols also knows that her quick wit, command of the word, and rather progressive views are daunting to the more timid male suitors. By 1873 Kate Nichols had been fully primed for "suitable" male attention and a good marriage. The stage was set.

Bubbling up from the past: Kate's re-created scene of how she and Spencer met. She was not aware then, but loves the story told to her later.

Beautiful and breezy, she is caught in the ray of sunlight at the door of the party, and immediately deified by the unobserved figure of successful Mr. Trask, watching from behind a curtain. An older man, perhaps thirty, tall, commanding, confident, quite well dressed. To his companion, the successful and very eligible bachelor Spencer Trask announces his plan: "Do you see that lady there, the one in the doorway… I plan to have her as my wife."

With purpose and drive, young and worldly Spencer had sought out his lady, obtained the proper introduction, satisfied the father, and won the girl. All made easier for families moving in similar social circles, espousing the same values, enjoying the same privileges. How had they missed each other in their mutual Sunday School projects? Perhaps the differences in age. She was at home nurturing her mind with Shakespeare and the Bible, British poems of imagination, faith, and nature, plus treatises on philosophy and tales of the Middle Ages — her much-favored subject. He was in the world opening his own prestigious investment firm, risking capital to support inventions not yet proven: he the denizen of new art galleries, the dashing and unmarried and quite impressive Mr. Trask! It was a marriage destined to be!

Very soon the fine wedding in Brooklyn, November 12, 1874, and the first house (more simple, but well located) for aristocratic newlyweds on Willow Street. The wedding trip abroad and those first months of married bliss, discovering the mysteries of bodies and sensations... her own physical desires tweaked by Romantic notions of courtly love, of maidens honored on jousting fields, of sweet bodily surrendering to new and powerful forces. Apart from Spencer's strong physical presence and the delicious feeling of lying in his arms, there is... all this OTHER about him.

She can make a mental list. The raised eyebrow of supreme confidence which melts away any opposition to his will, and his knowledge of the arts. He is moved by the Italian Renaissance painters and can explain why, knows particularly well Jacobean furniture, wants to start a National Arts Club or some entity to recognize promise and perhaps promote talent in budding artists... "Have you seen the work of that Rodin?" he would say. His talent for backing good business people and propositions ("This idea of Thomas Alva Edison, Kate... our firm backs him and we can illuminate all of New York... no, all the world.") His amazing financial finesse for his young age ("All the West's there for the taking: silver, gold mines, railroad tracks hauling the country's goods from coast to coast and back again.") The moral rectitude which infuses this wealthy man of many talents and possessions, yet in his pocket at all times is a folded note which reads "Beware of covetousness: for a man's life consisteth not in the abundance of the things which he possesseth."

How she LOVES him. All this in one irresistible package... and it creates for young Kate Trask a sense of supreme satisfaction with her mate, and with herself for having been chosen by him. It's as though they have been given a higher calling to be the couple *extraordinaire*, the golden couple with talents and noble plans to cut a fine swath in the world. There's work to do out there; she can't wait to launch their life.

Kate's memory also, time after time, falls upon Foster, steadfast George Foster Peabody, Spencer's handsome young friend in Brooklyn who became his best friend for life, as well as his future business partner. And Kate knows she has been loved by him from the beginning: from the early days they together explored "good works" projects for the church school; from the days he accidentally passed her on her own street; from the times he almost framed a case for himself as a suitor, but withdrew in the sad fact of his penury. Kate knows there ultimately was no choice but to have the older, confident, wealthy and dynamic Mr. Trask, promising exciting vistas and unlimited opportunities.

Foster had not come to their wedding. He had been absent earlier at the reception announcing their wedding plans. But a lady knows what the eyes say, how his eyes still lower in her presence to avoid the shameful knowledge of his yearnings for her. How hard for Foster to stay their friends, to continue loving *her* and respecting *them* and being in her presence so often while masking and utterly subduing such feelings. And how she basks in her husband's story, proving his trust of his friend and his love for her:

"Spencer, I am flattered you have asked me to become your partner and join your firm, but I have a confession to make. I am in love with your wife."

"And I don't blame you at all, Foster. I'm in love with her myself."

And like that, Foster, Spencer and I have built a firm and unique friendship. We three are bound by admiration and respect and utter devotion. Spencer is the man of action, the doer of great things. Foster and I FEEL with great intensity and lean toward the same values... education for the underprivileged, respite for the overworked, care for the unprotected. In perfect harmony we three love the Beautiful, in good works, but also in objects of art, paintings, furniture, literature. Spencer is the steady glow; Foster and I are the lightning, full of quick emotion and intensity. Foster and I are two sides of the same coin. And we love Spencer with our whole beings.

Now flickering on the ceiling of that bedroom in Brooklyn, images of Foster, Spencer and her own self, a portrait of three intimate friends, a comforting scene, and she feels a smile come to her lips:

For the last fifteen years we were together at our home in the evenings, sharing the firm's business developments, news articles from the New York Times, and laughing at the antics of the Astors and their sycophants. All those books and magazines in our living room, stacked here and there, waiting for us to discuss the art scene, the common denominator of world religions, the new inventions and their transforming potential for everyday life, and, Foster's favorite, the educational needs of the Negro in a newly emergent South. (This from his southern roots in Georgia, the haunting remembrance of the Civil War which ruined his family's livelihood and brought him north.)

Spencer and I so much like Foster's wonderful mind, his clear and balanced insight, all nourished in the nightly reading at his own "alma mater," the Brooklyn Y. M. C. A. How quickly had come his leap into learning and wisdom, without losing his sense of obligation to others… it brought us three together. And I am aware, always aware of Foster's shy hand brushing my fingers as he regales us with his recent adventures out West for the firm and shows us the latest Remington Indian illustrations in Harper's magazine. Spencer had encouraged my "drawing out" his shy friend in the beginning. Now with young Mr. Peabody's fine mind honed, his talents recognized, and his new fortune growing as a full partner in Spencer Trask and Company, our closest friend had eased into the Trask household without a ripple.

Most nights it was the three of us, conversing and alive with weighty ideas, lap rugs and tea before a crackling fire. Then we were a gay trio dissolving into charades and silly verse-making, we three so happy and content in our self-made universe. George Foster Peabody: the object of pure Man Love for Spencer. And how do I describe my kind of love for him? We three, the chaste ménage á trois? I only know I love the THREE of us together. Foster, dear, you've loved me forever, but loved Spencer MORE. And dear Foster, it is YOUR image I describe in my humble little stories and plays of the Middle Ages. Did you know it was YOU on the pages, you were the model of chivalrous knighthood in my poetry? You, there with Spencer, our revered King Arthur.

Medicine to take, she hears. Shadows in the room, shapes moving about and voices speaking in muffled tones. Feeling of cotton, a blanket, a grasping hand, a breeze stirring somewhere... outside the window in the elm tree? Have I slept a little? Am I better today?

Christina, is that you darling? Brown curls, grave face. Don't be sad, my darling. Mama's getting better. Christina? My wise daughter... have I created my mirror image and filled a young head with too many serious notions? Our family friend Mr. Blaine is behind this all,[1] admonishing me as a young Kate to study every day, to fill my head with knowledge and ideas and not the silly stuff of finishing schools and ladies' parlors... useless, useless froth.

Education: my duty as a mother, to educate and inspire the next generation... to realize the special Power bestowed on women. Our saucy little Christina has no silliness in her head. Beware twentieth century! Another intrepid lady is preparing for her assignment in the New World. My little lady is wise for her years, and she is a Christian saint. She writes and interprets verse, studies her Bible, and only two years ago she wrote a will. Can you IMAGINE a nine year old making a will in all earnestness? I marvel at her faith and her insight and the poem she wrote, only a year ago. Christina's poem. The woman by the child is taught. I must not be afraid.

> *"Grim death, thou art very near,*
> *But still I do not fear to have Thee come.*
> *Then life's strife will be o'er,*
> *I then will be far, far up in the blue sky,*
> *Far, far away.*
> *No mortal's hand can reach,*
> *No eye can pierce through the great portals, white,*
> *Far, far up in Heaven, far, far away."[2]*

Kate Trask has a most treasured and recurring image which floats before her eyes during these days of fever. It is shingled villa shaded by enormous fir trees. It is her favorite place, the rambling country home just a train ride up the Hudson River, past Albany. The 1850s Queen Anne "cottage" sitting in the heart of four hundred wild acres abutting, ironically, the fast-growing spa city Saratoga Springs.

Saratoga Springs: home to salubrious mineral waters, glamorous race track, gambling casinos, "summer social pretenders" (the gangster and the *parvenu*) as well as solid citizens. Wide treed avenues and the renown Grand Union Hotel, with its hundreds of rooms and its sixty-five-piece dance orchestra. Saratoga, the new American society itself: the place where all the optimistic, newly rich, happily extravagant Americans, some 50,000 of them, come each year to celebrate a giddy Gilded Age summer of pleasure. A glorious future lies ahead, it is certain, for the Vanderbilt grandsons as well as Mr. Canfield and his stylish new casino. But the well-known summer resident Mrs. Trask, when queried, much prefers a quiet family life at her secluded mansion on the edge of town.

She will not go down to the Grand Union Hotel, or any other, to mingle with socialites and "the fashionable." She will not join the procession of carriages every afternoon to make the *de rigueur* drive to Lake Saratoga, nor will she make a studied promenade down Broadway as part of the renowned display of over-blown fashion and foolishness. She chooses wandering the vast pine forests, stepping over spring-fed brooks, hiking to the top of the hill to see Vermont in the distance and the beginning of the Adirondack Mountains to the north. She will have no idle chatter about people, but will listen to Nature's creatures conversing in the woodlands. She is a true Romantic of the nineteenth century, a child of Nature. Nature inspires and instructs her, not the dictates of fashion and frivolity, and certainly not empty gossip.

Images of Kate's country villa have filled her drifting memory for days now. The old house, sprawling and rundown, with no running water, broken latches, sagging steps and a few harmless snakes from the surrounding woods. It had been a fortuitous rental for a grieving family in black who had buried their first born, and blamed the city and its ills. Kate for several years had brought little Christina and, later, new brother Junius here to the safety of the country for spring, summer, and early fall. She had fallen in love with the Romantic ideal of simple, country life. And it was far from the foul air and filth of the city.

The rambling house was called the Childs Mansion, built on the older-still Barhyte farm. To add to its rough but stylish appeal was the fact that it had some literary history, too: it was said that Edgar Allen Poe had created *The Raven* while visiting the former owners there. After a happy summer of renting the place, Kate had discovered it might be for sale — and had laughed at Spencer's misgivings over the thought of purchasing. But she had used her wiles, and her dear husband had put his mind to it. If anyone could make that house happen for her, Spencer could. And some weeks later — she still in the country, he in the city — as she packed boxes amid falling leaves and heavy thoughts of leaving Paradise and returning to ordered social life, Kate had received the telegram from Spencer:

"Mrs. Spencer Trask. Saratoga Springs,
New York. Hail, Mistress of Yaddo."

Kate likes the story of the naming of Yaddo, this new country retreat. She one day will write a history of Yaddo and their summer life, and will share this with family and friends. Beautiful four-year-old Christina had named it, calling out her choice of a name for the place after careful exaggerated ruminating, with eyes tightly closed.

"I was sitting in the somber setting of our living room in Brooklyn... when I remarked to Christina, playing nearby... and I said, 'and what shall we name the place, Cuckoo?'"

"Now I know... Call it Yaddo, Mama, for it makes poetry! Yaddo, shadow, shadow, Yaddo! It sounds like shadow but it's not going to be shadow."[3]

Christina's cheerful nature had suffered in a sad and lifeless household grieving for older brother Alanson. Curtains drawn, they were living in the shadows: shadow was the setting for their sadness. She longed for light and gaiety and exuberant living again.

And so Yaddo it would be, the funny name that was not shadow.

The most wonderful thing in Kate's romantic life officially had been christened. It would become her Heart's Home, not the townhouse in Brooklyn or the big house in Tuxedo Park. They had set about altering the ungainly old house and taming the wildness of the forest around it. Loving landscape architecture, Spencer had personally created new walking paths, carriageways, configurations of trees and flower-beds. He had dammed streams, begun trout hatcheries, planted vegetable gardens. He had built barns, an ice house, outbuildings to make the country farm a self-sufficient estate for his household. They were living the healthful country dream.

Kate had, with Foster's good eye, selected ornamentation and architectural additions to make the building more artistic and commodious. From a deserted, decaying house emerged a wonderful country home for the Trask family, a family they intended to expand. Another son for the family. The house full of children's poems and toys, objects of art and *kitsch* collected from Europe and the American West, the routine filled with family ceremonies and pageantry orchestrated by Spencer for his queen, for his Katrina Regina... this house symbolized for Kate Trask love, family, and the Future.

And now in her drifting mind, Life comes to the forefront, family life. Colorful and vivid scenes of the

Trask Family at Yaddo. She suddenly, happily, is living a scrapbook of memorabilia: the summers of pony rides and birthday parties (the little paper hats and stick horse favors) and parlor games and posing for photos, when Spencer and Mr. Eastman Johnson alternated as photographer ("Papa's are the best, Mama"), and servant songfests and Christmas plays with the entire household staff, and the week-long festivities going on with music and twinkly lights, ending with elaborate Twelfth Night pageants. Medieval costumes, horns, court jesters and white doves. The Christmas season, the sublime crowning event of life at Yaddo. Pageantry, music, blazing fireplace, cinnamon and ginger from the kitchen. The wide-eyed poor children from the local school invited in with their teachers, blinking to see the interior of Yaddo and to enjoy, just for the afternoon of a holiday, the gaiety and style of the very rich. For each visiting child, their own name inscribed, an undreamed-of present wrapped in crimson tissue, bound with golden cord and smelling of pine from the Lady of Yaddo.

She smiles, remembering Christina's pride in family life and Yaddo pageantry.

"Papa writes plays like Mama does, and once near All Saints Eve he made Mama the Queen of Yaddo. It was our surprise for her... and Papa wrote the pageant script. All day she was sequestered in her room. The library was wrapped in medieval banners, the candelabras held flickering candles, and Grandma, and Uncle, and Junius and

I and all the household waited at the bottom of the stair-case, autumn leaves covering the rail, and she was brought down, so astonished. Then on the arm of Papa she was led to a real throne in the library, and given a ring, a crown and a scepter. Mama SO lovely in the trailing white gown she was given, the one with fur cuffs, with all her jewels. We were ALL in costume... Papa in purple velvet with white plumes on his hat and I in my blue satin dress which Miss Pardee selected for the pageant. And Junius looking lost in his medieval cape. Papa, in such the elegant voice, kneeled and called out, 'Hail to thee, Katrina Regina'."

Kate still demurs, embarrassed by the name.
Queen? QUEEN?

So against my principles, you know. Queen... king... and I the democrat. The world is fighting kings and queens. The world must know this name of queen was never mine to choose. They must think me so self-centered. But I can't protest when so much LOVE was bestowed in the naming. I can't resist the game when the players give it with such gen-erosity of heart. And so I accept the title: Katrina Regina. Lady of Yaddo.
Perhaps a pen name for my writing:
Katrina? Katrina Trask.
So many memories...
Nighttime... Daytime... Nighttime. Daytime?

I can swallow.

Liquid tracing its way slowly down the
battered corridor.

More water please.

*How long have I been in this demi-world, half sleep-
ing, half awake? I'm getting well. No more shackles on my
throat. Spencer? Dr. Gibbons?*
Almost there… try to get back.

April 12, 1888: Kate Nichols Trask recovers from
the fever, and learns that upstairs on the third floor
her children have been infected. Her son is dying. Her
daughter is desperately ill. There are strange new nurses
whose faces she has never seen. Outside her room there
are sounds of footsteps on the stairs, doctors coming
and and going to the third floor, fighting the poison.
And then she is allowed upstairs, at last, to find a weak
boy sleeping, a pale daughter smiling, pink ribbon tied
about her throat, "so I shall be bright for Mama."

April 15, 1888: Sunday. Little Junius, Spencer Trask, Jr., the only living son, dies of diphtheria in his fifth year.

April 18, 1888: Daybreak, Wednesday. In an early morning vigil, the mother watches her last child drift away to Heaven. Christina Trask dies of diphtheria in her eleventh year.

NO. NO. My dearest Jesus, you who were supremely HUMAN, and who suffered… with your hand in mine I battled Evil and was the victor. I survived. But my life has suffered an unspeakable tragedy. I am forsaking you, Jesus! I see no resurrection in MY life. It is done. My soul's companion I name Grief. ❁

Chapter One

Coming to Terms

My soul lay lifeless in the beginning. Because grief is an all-consuming, selfish thing, I thought of my children's deaths as my own during those first days after the burial. The claiming of my babies was a searing personal calamity; my heart and soul had been ripped from my body while I slept. I had been violated by the Devil himself and I felt paralyzed to show emotion, to validate my own existence by weeping or speaking. My soup had no taste; I felt neither warmth nor chill. The days breaking bright and beautiful were no different from the terrorizing and endless nights where I floated in an abyss. The spring chirp of birds outside my window brought me pain; I closed the curtains. The sound of school children whistling or singing in the street below signaled a new headache. I could not wrap my thoughts around Spencer's grief, because I could not understand my own. Life was an illusion, a phantom which had maliciously lured me on and then abandoned me just as I perceived some meaning. Our family with the fortune of money and intellect was being positioned to do good in the world, to live life grandly and purposefully. My children were glittering gifts meant to outshine their progenitors. My Christina, my Junius were uniquely blessed. They were full of potential perfection in their brilliant little lives, and they were slapped down by an indifferent hand. Butterflies on a bright leaf trampled by a crude boot. I buried my children in that grassy spot and tried to return to life, but I was not alive at all.

I was angry at Spencer, at God, at life around me, life seemingly unscathed, oblivious to my injury. Did NO ONE understand?

"Time does NOT bring relief." My voice was loud and angry. My arms were tight at my side, and Spencer, surprised at my outburst, my first spark of emotion, moved towards me. Finally, after weeks, I had dressed and come down to the drawing room and he was surprised.

"I see Junius cross-legged by the desk in your library, lining his toy soldiers for battle. I hear Christina's voice when I walk past the nursery, her sing-song rhymes, the scratch of her little gold pen against paper. And I push open the door to rush to her, and..."

"My dearest love, it is NOT all done." Spencer reached to me, but I pulled away.

"MY life is done. I feel it is all finished for me. I've lost my will. My soul dropped into those small spaces in the earth where they lay our children, soon bones next to their brother's."

My brittle, cold body ached from tension and frustration. I had shunned my friends and shrunk from my husband's touch, angrily sent away the minister, isolated myself into a safe and secret and dark place. I was a cracked dish about to explode into shards if I felt the heat of any emotion. My pride had been in my strength, but even my strength now was failing. So alone. So lost. I felt myself falling, broken and vulnerable into my husband's arms. Spencer's power and courage were the safe port for my rudderless and damaged skiff of a life. For the first time in weeks I could feel the weight of his arms around me: I could feel the faint stirrings of a sense of touch.

"Then HELP me, please. Spencer, please help me."

"Dear, dear Kate. I tell you what you have only forgotten. Reclaim your faith and your trust in Christ. It is what I have had to keep me from drowning. The thought of losing you was... if I ever lost you... I could never...."

For the first time since our tragedy I actually looked into Spencer's eyes and felt his own anguish. He had lost three children, and he was losing his wife. I began to listen to his words.

"This I HAVE to believe. This we must hang on to and never forsake. This concept, this Faith, which is all we have. There is a vast purpose we cannot yet see. You and I act out our small drama on a minor stage in Brooklyn, New York. Our drama, my darling, is a beautiful, but small one in a churning, turning, large world, and God is directing the workings of that world. Trust what you cannot see and re-arm yourself. Reclaim your faith, my beloved."

"I loved Christ and his humanity, and he took away my children," I offered in measured tones.

"We will fill the nursery again, you and I, and we

will feel Christ's blessing. Our children are dead, my beloved lady, but Christ is not dead, Kate. And you and I are still here."

Then, suddenly, my heart burst and I let the tears come, a torrent held back for weeks. I sobbed uncontrollably, and Spencer, too, let go his burden of despair and we held each other tightly, and sank to the floor in that big room on the small stage of the big world. We held on, rocking, and sobbing together for a long time, two souls there in the evening, purging our grief and praying for relief and a better morning.

My returning faith, and my husband, and the children's most esteemed nanny Allena were my constant companions for those difficult summer months. I could not bear for Allena to leave us. She was the high-spirited lady who came to care for our children and live in our house. Tall, lovely, whimsical but practical, full of sparkle and charm, Allena never left my side in those bleak days. She was not family, but she had become a necessary part of the household, and she became each day more and more my companion and confidant. I knew how devoted she was to me. I had seen her dare overwhelming wrath for the sake of loyalty to us, meet horrid situations with her lovely smile, stand at her post in the midst of raging disease and pestilence, and never, never say an unkind word about anyone. I had often compared her nature to that of my husband: a delicious mix of New England seriousness with French gaiety and charm.[4] With her encouragement, and that of Spencer's I began to write of the children during the summer and fall. It was the beginning of my on-going *Chronicles of Yaddo*, full of family history, remembrances of the children, story of Yaddo's origins. The writing of my *Chronicles of Yaddo* was meant to be a way of working through the pain, a catharsis, gradually accepting the wrenching reality of my tragedy, and celebrating the beauties of our family when we were whole. The *Chronicles of Yaddo 1888* was full of jagged emotions. My first page:

> *"I sometimes hold it half a sin*
> *To put in words the grief I feel;*
> *For words, like Nature, half reveal*
> *And half conceal the Soul within."*[5]

I exposed my heart, but I requested privacy. Please, this is not to be published like some of my poems and plays. It is meant for only my family and closest friends. And so I continued my *Chronicles*, writing a little each day.

I recalled little snippets of scenes from Christina's childhood, she dressed in her Marie Antoinette costume and living out the drama of the queen's end, going bravely to her death, unafraid because "Mama, heaven is just so beautiful." Christina with jutting chin was unafraid of Death; her sole reservation was only that Mama and Papa and Junius should miss her. Christina, who kept Longfellow's *Hiawatha* in her Locked Book along with a turned down page: "Faith shineth as a morning star."[6] And I wrote, "How could sorrow be borne without a power stronger than our own — without a faith to see beyond the present pain, and trust that what we know not now we shall know later."[7] I remembered my saintly daughter as she nurtured her own brother, stepping aside to let him shine, holding back so he could be first, living at such a young age such a Christ-like example. Writing my memories of my children, Christina's saintliness banished my sorrow each day. While I jotted in my journal, Allena, without being asked, became my surrogate lady of the house. She replied to my correspondence in her perfect tone, ordered the rose bouquets for the parlor, organized menus in the kitchen which pleased a distracted husband and wife somehow getting through difficult days. She opened the curtains in the children's rooms and let the sunlight wash over the dusty toy soldiers and Christina's guitar. Sometimes I heard her beautiful voice singing from the third floor and it made me — yes, it made me smile.

That winter was made bearable because, miraculously, we were expecting a new babe. God was giving us a new opportunity. Our family had not been forgotten, and there was a sense of heightened expectation for this birth as we this year welcomed a beautiful spring. This baby would thrive in a late summer at Yaddo. It would bask in sunlight in its bassinet at Yaddo, the little white wicker bed brought outside so it could gaze up through fir trees into bright skies, watching with baby-eyes shafts of light through the pines near the terrace... stimulus for new baby's eyes. Breezes from Yaddo on smooth little cheeks, and the smell of tea roses from the east garden. Charmed baby in a charmed life.

We celebrated the birth of a our baby girl Katrina in the summer of 1889, and cried together as God reclaimed her in only a few days. She would not be an offering to replace our Christina. This tiny creature would be returned to Heaven hardly able to have tasted, felt, heard life. Her little eyes had never opened. Spencer and I stood at graveside again with my family and his, and with Foster and some other close friends, swallowing salty tears. Before us, on the grassy Brooklyn plot under a summer sky were four little graves. They quietly and innocently marked The End. I knew my body besieged by heart troubles would never bear another child. This was to be the end of all grand plans for the Spencer Trask Family and its legacy.

> *Christ, you ask too much of your servant;*
> *you must buttress me with supreme human Faith.*

Spencer was quieter now, in the August days that followed. He seemed weakened. A soldier home from battle but broken in spirit, less able to meet his days with confidence. He voiced his faith, but clearly it had been shaken when we lost yet another child. Four times we had buried little creatures with Spencer's eyes, my chin, the outward promise of our family's future.

Curiously it was I who felt empowered to give solace this time. It was as though I was waiting for the Reason, the Plan, the Purpose in our lives. I steeled myself to be highly tuned and expectant, waiting for direction, pliant with a willing and open heart. I would *intellec-*

tualize our lives, eschew large emotions, and proceed with rational thinking. Perhaps a Trask Family Legacy was not meant to be. Many individuals had no children of their own, I told myself reasonably. For those who did, child mortality was all too prevalent, among the mighty *and* the lowly. The "small drama" of my loss had been shared by so many, in so many lands. While I waited for some sense of direction, for events or ideas to make a life's path for us, I thought of ways to fill the hours. We were more fortunate than most, freed, if we so chose, from labor and a daily schedule. Spencer had in Foster the perfect partner and friend who would stay in New York and run the firm and make the decisions if we should need a voyage away.

I had begun to think of sailing for Europe. We both loved art, architecture, travel, languages. We had friends. Lord Chittenden and Lady Milhouse would be happy to receive us, and Count Brioni in Perugia had insisted on a visit to Umbria some years ago. It was time for another trip to Firenze, and to Lake Como, Bellagio with its misty lake banked by Switzerland's mountains. We had hoped one day to take the tortuous Amalfi drive and stay at the Grand Hotel dei Cappuccino near Ravello, to see the petrified figures caught in time at Pompeii, to walk the high paths of Capri wreathed in *bougainvillea*. We both desired to browse through antiquity in the Museo Nazionale in Naples. And what glory to ferry across the Straits of Messina where Sirens beckoned Ulysses, to stroll among Greek temple ruins in Syracusa lemon groves. Yes, and to sit thoughtfully in Taormina's monumental Greek theatre ruins, their sturdy arches a foil to Mt. Aetna smoldering in the background. It would be so inspiring. It would be so *distracting*. We should go to Europe for an extended period! As soon as possible, I said. As soon as possible.

I did not have to be persuasive: Spencer was in favor of the idea. My family's friend James Blaine was Secretary of State, and within weeks we had a State Department-issued passport for Mr. Spencer Trask and his wife. Foster would take over the running of the Edison Illuminating Company, which had been moved to the offices of Spencer Trask and Company on Broad Street when Spencer was named the second president. Spencer had also helped to finance Edison Electric Illuminating of Brooklyn. Both companies were finally becoming a good investment, even paying quarterly dividends.[8] Foster would manage perfectly in Spencer's absence. We cabled our European friends, organized our affairs, reserved our suite on the new luxury German ocean liner *Teutonic,* and sailed out of New York harbor at the end of December, heading with icy winds into the new decade of 1890. The last ten years of the great century, certainly, would be good ones for the Trasks. There was much to see and learn in this new world: changing forms of art, advances in communication and transportation, ideas of reform and justice; and Mr. and Mrs. Trask had the means and the time to examine our place in it all. We were off!

Our new-found optimism did not last: Fate had other plans for Spencer and me not long after our return from abroad. By the spring of 1891, there would be another disaster lying in wait for us. We were a rare and privileged couple to the on-looking world, but our inner lives were full of disasters and recoveries. Fate seemed to design a daunting labyrinth for us, and our constitutions and our faith were challenged continually. This next tragic event was almost too horrid to understand and accept.

On this one raw April day we were in the city, and Spencer was quite ill with pneumonia. And in Saratoga that very morning a barbaric fire had invaded our home, was licking its way through our Yaddo, racing through the corridors and over the roof, consuming the lovely shingled cottage with hellish red flames and heavy black smoke. When Foster arrived with the news that evening, I was reading beside a warming fire while Spencer slept. Foster came with a pale face, and strong arms, and the dreaded news. I silently asked myself how much more our family must endure. Before my eyes flashed the devastating images, our country home and its cherished memories burned to the ground. It was what we had left of our family together, and that which we most loved.

I tried to create in my mind the horrid scene in Saratoga. Was there a foundation left? Towering gaunt chimneys still standing, violated and ashamed? Would household items be strewn about, toys and rocking horse buried in ashes next to silver urns and crockery? The paintings, curled and blackened in their gilded frames? Was there ANYTHING left? How did it start?

Was anyone hurt? I imagined the group of fir trees and hedges which must be damaged on the north side, now skeletons without their green raiments.

But Foster, we can't tell Spencer this news. He is really no better today than yesterday. This pneumonia hangs on, and the news... will kill him. We can't.

The truth was that Foster knew his friend's strengths. The two thought as one. They had shared business decisions and were sensitive to one another's approaches to solving problems, always arriving at a balanced solution. We made the decision and brought the dreaded news to his bedside.

In a weak but decisive voice, Spencer had given orders.

"Telegraph at once for the photographer to go out to Yaddo and take plenty of photographs. I want to see the ruins. We shall need many pictures of the foundations when we make the plans for the new house and I shall not be able to travel for some time."[9]

While Spencer regained his strength, Foster steered me through the immediate business details of planning for a new house, and spoke of the future with excitement. We busied ourselves with many of the smaller practical details, but Spencer soon recovered and had obviously envisioned some well-thought-out grand scenarios from his sickbed. We looked at plans of English country estates. Lists of architects were drawn up, queries were made, nights were spent leafing through art books and our own European photographs of details such as fountains, arches, paneling, staircases. We looked at our photos of fountains from

Ravello, friezes from the Museo Nazionale. This would not be a patchwork renovation like we had made with the old Queen Anne cottage. This would be OUR plan, our child. We both knew the new Yaddo would be more perfectly tuned to our personal desires in style, size, and elegance. I had been tutored in taste from my childhood, and had been "the American cousin" at several English country estates during our travels abroad. Spencer and I appreciated beauty of design, classic harmony and perfection in detail. And we both loved the Medieval period. We knew the English manor we would duplicate and already had plans in our head for our Gothic estate in the country.

We had to have a look at the foundation ruins with our new plans, to make some decisions about expanding the floor plan, and what direction it would take. We expected that our first look at the ruins would be too much to bear, but a most miraculous thing happened as our carriage horses clip-clopped up the rain-soaked driveway for the first view of the destruction. *"What a morose mood we were in as we drove from the rail-station, but when we passed through the gates at Yaddo, suddenly the sun burst forth and we clasped hands tightly, wondering what would be ahead around the next curve. We reached the ruins, and as we took in the charred destruction, suddenly the most beautiful rainbow that I have ever seen spanned that blackened mass."*[10] The arc blessed us with its symbol of rebirth.

Another harbinger of good fortune presented itself to me some time after this. It was a simple little verse from a book given to me at the birth of Alanson. Some unseen force seemed to direct me to find that book, which I had put away in Brooklyn for some time. I had opened that little book, a memento of my first-born child, thinking sadly of the other items of our children which had been destroyed in the fire. I was holding the book and turned to the day of our expected visit to the ruin, thinking *this will be an omen for me and for the new house.* The first thing I saw was a spiritual verse which I took for my own personal interpretation: *"The glory of this latter House shall be greater than that of the former, and in this place will I give Peace."*[11] I resolved that this inscription should be in the cornerstone of the new Yaddo.

After that we were full of expectations and busy with all the drawings, plans, and notes we had devised ourselves. Yaddo would be expansive. It would be granite, Gothic with Medieval touches which Spencer and I both appreciated. It seemed that because of my weak constitution — the recurring heart problems which appeared, then resided — we were destined never to have a family again. It would not do for Spencer and me to dream of future generations of Trasks bringing their little ones here, celebrating life's occasions with joy and pageantry. This sad acceptance which we had come to own since we stood mutely at that graveside now became the impetus for our frantic outburst of energy which helped us build our fifty-five-room home. The architect would work with our design to make a house spacious enough for many, many friends and for our own siblings, nieces and nephews. It would be a place of beauty and tranquility, rooms where we would celebrate art and hang our portraits of the children, a room for music, a grand library with fireplace, and a dining room large enough for formal dinners for twenty or thirty, a beautiful room as a backdrop for lively dinner conversation. And we would share this new Yaddo, the one "greater than the house before" with the community, welcoming good people from all social levels, and especially welcoming children. We would share our walking paths which Spencer had carved out of the wilds, the small lakes at the end of woodland paths, the lakes named for our children, and the benches for quiet reflection during a hot summer.

The home would be modeled on historic Haddon Hall in the English countryside, a grey stone mansion suggesting the Middle Ages, knights, heraldry. There would be a baronial Great Hall passing through the center of the house, sweeping its way to a wide outdoor terrace and vistas beyond. This space would bisect the building with doors opening off on either side, to the dining room, to the front parlor, and to the bay-windowed library with a commodious fireplace and walls housing our collection of books on history, art, literature.

We commissioned an intricately-carved staircase ascending from the hall, and on the landing Spencer had our friend Louis Comfort Tiffany design a stained glass window to create a wall of sunlight, its allegorical figure Hope raising her arms forward, to be guided towards the north star. Mr. Tiffany also designed a multi-layered stained-glass window in the entrance, shedding colored light on the fountain and Hebe statue. Here the subject matter was adapted from my own small story from native Indian lore, the story of Winnapoca and Minneo.[12] In my upstairs room he designed a bay window with the single rose motif, my own personal symbol which evoked chivalrous love. Mr. Tiffany also created for us a mosaic panel over the Great Hall fireplace. In it was a phoenix rising from the ashes and the inscription *Flammis invicta per ignem Yaddo resurgo ad pacem:* Unconquered by flame, I, Yaddo, am reborn for peace.[13]

We furnished the mansion with some of our favorite European antiques including some ecclesiastical pieces,[14] but we happily mixed ornate mahogany and Jacobean formality with summer wicker and whimsical worthless travel treasures which brought us joy. We knew the rules of decoration, and knowing them, we could break them. We were not a couple to slavishly follow trends or fads: our home expressed ourselves and our ideals.

Among the features of our new Yaddo, Spencer designed for me the Tower Room with arched ceiling, Medieval niches, a wall of windows framing the mountains, trees, and sky. (Thoughtfully, he planned for Allena's room to adjoin mine; she would enjoy the same far-reaching views to the east.) Spencer had been encouraging my writing, my creative spirit. I had published my earlier works anonymously in Britain, not wanting to "push the boundaries" of gender, or possibly detract from Spencer's business reputation were I found "lacking." But as I gained some honor and recognition "anonymously," I became more confident, published some pieces here, and Spencer was my greatest enthusiast. The tower was my writing room, my sanctuary where I could be isolated to create. In this room I would soon begin to write more: a play about King Arthur, some verses in the vein of the Romantic poets in Britain... Shelley, Keats, Wordsworth. A few daring American women were writing in the Realist vein, exposing the ugly in an industrial and urban society about to mark a centennial. But I had witnessed "unseemly" and "unfair" in my personal life and cared not to dwell on them. And I found a heroism in the Medieval period which lifted my spirits. I worried not if my verse seemed to some "overly sentimental" or if some critics disliked my didactic plays; there were so many positive critiques, so much praise in papers from abroad when my identity was known, that my talents seemed indeed validated. My literary creations in verse or story were peopled with good characters acting nobly, or less good characters being forgiven. Husbands and wives coming to understand one another. Love and forgiveness. And I wanted my verse to be dignified, yet descriptive of real human emotions. In 1894 a quite nice book of my sonnets and lyrics was published, to some acclaim. My little book on marriage and forgiveness, *Free Not Bound*, had been positively reviewed.

Perhaps later I would use my pen to make a political difference in the world. Deep within were "democratic" ideas I was still trying to crystallize; my heart was showing me the bigotry and injustice in the world but I was not yet strong enough to take a stand. I was a lady blessed with material wealth, but fate had been cruel to me and I was still trying to heal, to piece my broken personal life into a semblance of whole. After all, I was schooled as a proper Victorian lady who serenely commanded her clearly-defined space. The English queen's code of "acceptable behavior" washed over the American shore with an indisputable force. A strong and fearless woman was required to mount an assault on social and political problems. I was not prepared to do this. Yet.

Though I was not a zealous *writer* for social change at that time, I did have philanthropic instincts for social reform which helped women and their children. I became a contributing member of the Kindergarten Association in New York city which provided for childcare for working women. Spencer supported some funds which helped working women with medical expenses. We spread our philanthropy among a wide range of social needs in New York and abroad. My husband himself rallied to the cause of the Christian Armenians persecuted by the Muslim Turks and alerted the whole nation to the need for funds. He became treasurer of the Armenian Relief Committee and was in contact with Clara Barton in Constantinople as she described the relief work there. Spencer's committee raised $100,000 for the cause and he and I became a stalwart admirer of Miss Barton who took the Red Cross to Turkey during this dreadful time. He himself went on speaking tours to awaken Americans to the atrocities against women and children in particular, and to plead for financial assistance. Here is a woman you would love, my husband wrote once, because of her hatred of war. And I did come to value her work done under great danger and deprivation in foreign realms. I admired her resilience under pressure, a lone woman with the nerve and resolve to "do," not just "say."

Saratoga country life had began in earnest for the Trasks in the early 1880s. Each season Spencer and I set about spending longer periods of time at our first Yaddo, entertaining, involving ourselves more in the town of Saratoga Springs. Spencer opened an office in the "spa city," knowing wealthy visitors in the summer would need a good investment firm nearby. And when we took up a private campaign against the loathsome gambling in the casinos there, and warned of the vices in Congress Park (innocent young men preyed upon by wanton women) we had run into opposition from the town fathers. They knew their future income would be from the horse people and the gamblers and the summer hotel clients who came to hear Victor Herbert and his big orchestra, to stroll down Broadway and "be seen." Already the horse people were building lavish "cottages" up and down Broadway and along Union Avenue, and they spent freely in the stores and restaurants opening up in the last decades of our century.

The townspeople ignored us on the gambling issue, even claimed Spencer's business was "gambling" with clients' money, and we lost a good fight in the early days. The Canfield Casino remained a big pull for young men who left sullen after losing a fortune at the race track, and then tried their luck at the gambling houses. The Canfield stood lurid and defiant in the center of the park, surrounded by churches and a school, enticing the bad sort which Spencer and I thought compromised the bright future of Saratoga Springs. We saw Saratoga as a blessed spot because of the expansive views of hills and forests, the mild nurturing summers, the springs which the Indians had named "medicine waters" for their curative nature. Should fast money and the glitter of gold for a short span of months destroy the year-round natural gifts of the village?

Spencer preached, argued, organized meetings, and signed petitions with that odd reforming moralist from New York city Mr. Anthony Comstock. He had come to Saratoga to mount his attack on the gambling and we had come to his meeting (our mutual enemies make us friends?). Spencer bought a newspaper in Saratoga to express the dire peril. We even sought to alert the local farmers on the outskirts of town who wielded a vote and might not be aware of the dangers of gambling. Spencer and I late one night went in disguise (much to the alarm of our servants) in a market wagon to distribute pamphlets for the cause... our Midnight Ride we called it. All to no avail. The majority of Saratogians knew where their needed money was coming from and were not about to eliminate the source. Saratoga was bustling and thriving and becoming a destination for people from the South and the West coming to find a wealthy husband or wife, coming to see and be seen, coming for all the summer activities of balls, croquet, garden parties, concerts, swimming, boating, riding, horse racing, gambling. And, of course, the springs and the lovely weather.[15]

The Trasks had hoped to emphasize the latter, but we would have to wait for the election of Governor Charles Evans Hughes and some needed state legislation to end the scourge of gambling. Some decades later, Canfield Casino was given to the city for public use, the park beautified and "cleansed" of its past. Congress Park would become the elegant center of an elegant city. The Trasks would leave their mark on Congress Park and it would become an enchanting oasis for townspeople and their children and a safe and inviting haven for visitors. Some years after Spencer's death the town would place a striking statue — across from the casino, no less — honoring Mr. Trask who was not an enemy, but a visionary man who spent his life helping Saratoga reach its full potential.

In those early days there were other areas in town where we *could* make a difference. Our sadness at the loss of our children heightened our desire to be mindful of the needs of other children. "We shall establish a hospital here for sick children in the city, children who could never afford the luxury and healing powers of the country. It shall be Katrina's Home," Spencer announced one day. Spencer had a vision, made a decision, and made it happen. Our heart's gaping hole left from the loss of our children would be filled by local sick children, young orphans, children bereft of blessings, and Spencer and I reached out with a real thirst for the young people we could bless in some way.

My local philanthropy in the beginning chapters of Yaddo's history would be centered around a principle I cherished, a code of expectations and behavior which I demanded in my household. One's staff is one's family. At Yaddo, household service is a true profession which requires knowledge, skill, and efficiency. Understanding, compassion, and nurturing is meted out on a personal level to one's staff, but in return much is expected. One must be the BEST at whatever one does, no matter how humble.

Staff needed training, and there were local girls who needed guidance and tutoring to develop a career in household management. My personal mission was to open doors for poor women of good values to learn worthwhile skills. It was important that each profession, even household service, was a dignified form of labor, in which professionals took pride and were afforded dignity and personal respect. I was haunted by the spectacle of the poor women working in the sweat shops and factories in the industrial cities... New York, Troy just down the Hudson... the horrid conditions, the heat, the filth, the indecent pay, the long hours, the low level of worthiness they must feel. Our household of one-hundred plus was the practical proving-ground for my philosophy.

Our Yaddo staff was not to be treated as a "machine" or a race apart. Those who served us should have a place to sit of their own, a dining room, a place with books, music, art to uplift them. They who care for our personal needs, feed us, cook for us, need to be nurtured by us, in turn. If someone cooks, or cleans, or serves well, he deserves the same praise as an artist in any other line of endeavor.

In my household at Yaddo each servant had a private meeting with me as they joined our family.

My usual introduction:

"We have an esprit de corps here at Yaddo, Betty. Hopefully you will come to realize it is your JOY to serve here, like our Master came to serve. At Yaddo you are fortunate to have the opportunity to develop your profession's skills. Each of us has a duty to better ourselves, to develop some skill... domestic, artistic, mechanical... I write, you know, and avail myself of books, books and more books. Here you have such an environment to better yourself. It is UNIMPORTANT where you came from. Your environment can change you."

My society friends admonished me.

"You will rue the day," said an old family friend of mine, *"that you broke down the barriers of custom. You will spoil your servants, absolutely spoil them: you will see."*[16]

"Not at all. I have never been MORE dissatisfied with those in my employment than with those in any other stratum of society. With OTHERS, yes. I have never been deceived by my servants. With other professions, yes. Drunkards? Not my servants, but many a friend and social contact have behaved in a despicable manner."[17]

Spencer had to listen to my ranting and carrying-on in the study before dinner. I'm sure he preferred reading his papers or working on the plans for the Illumination Company but I tend to get on my latest topic of interest and insist on being heard. He would sit quietly at his desk, papers neatly stacked in piles, and I would pace before the fireplace, sparkling water cradled in hands, a dish of biscuits nearby, spouting my views, to myself? to him? to my future readers?

"My entire life I have bristled at those friends who have no sympathy, no compassion, no willingness to look beyond their own image in the mirror to see the utter foolishness of their conventional and bigoted lives. So many have no love and compassion for all God's people, only for those whom they select to love. Our Savior loved the Mighty and the Lowly; he gave his love to the aristocrat in equal portions to that of the lowest class. He was the ultimate Democrat, I say. When I look at a woman in need, she is my sister, Spencer. One who needs help is my sister."

No visible response.

"Society would be so much better if we could somehow offer opportunities for able women whose lives have been denied because of circumstances of birth."

"Ummm...," said Spencer.

"I am not suggesting that Jesus thought wealth in itself was a sin, nor poverty in itself a virtue. Rich and poor were his friends. He broke bread with both. I do object to groups, Democrats, Republicans, Socialists, Anarchists, Monarchists using Christ's gospel as a political or economic cure-all. They do not love their fellow man, but claim Christ is within them. Reformers today claim Jesus for their causes, but they never work for faith, hope, and charity."

I had another almond biscuit, and continued my charge.

"Dull convention is our prisoner. Hypocrisy reigns in America. How misguided are my friends who entreat me to give up my poetry and philosophy and attend to my church going and proselytizing for Protestantism. They piously entreat me, and they leave their coachmen outside in freezing rain for four hours while they sit in my warm parlor, feeling smug and selected by Jesus. I will spend my LIFE fighting against such attitudes. They preach 'the letter of the law in rule and canon' and entirely miss the spirit of true Christian living. So much of the world seems BLIND to the Truth."

"I quite agree, my love."

"I want to DO something practical here in Saratoga, I want to give women a profession that gives them dignity. Not the proverbial fish given to the masses, but training given to LEARN to fish. And to fish with dignity and proficiency. I want to make household service a recognizable and respected trade."

He was buried in his Broadway Realty files from the office. His thoughts were captured in managing the tallest office building in Lower Manhattan. He was trying to organize an arts society in the city to promote young American talent. He was the treasurer of a number of men's clubs. His mind was on the silver mines in the Southwest, a railroad matter with Mr. Gould, a hospital project with Mr. Rockefeller, the new Sugar Beet Company in California. But I knew he was listening to me, as well. I turned to absent myself, but not without bending towards him, white bosom to his soft brown hair, and delivering a most alluring kiss. He received it with growing enthusiasm. I pushed his papers aside.

In 1893 St. Christina's Home opened on Ballston Street in Saratoga Springs. Its mission would be the training of young women for household professions. They would enter the home at a young age and receive a sound education as well as practical training in sewing, cleaning, ironing, cooking, and serving properly. The lovely brownstone building also would be open to children from the hospital during the summer. We entrusted the direction of the school to the church sisterhood of the Episcopal Diocese of Albany. Spencer generously had given the funds and entreated other Saratoga friends to join in the cause. But it was my idea. The power of Woman, properly channeled, is not to be underestimated. ❊

Above: Spencer Jr., called Junius, on a donkey and Christina
on her horse. Standing girl is unidentified.
Below: Junius at Yaddo, Christina in a window, circa 1886.
{ Courtesy Saratoga Springs History Museum }

Christina, Junius, Katrina, and Spencer Trask
with dog Duke, 1885
{ Courtesy Saratoga Springs History Museum }

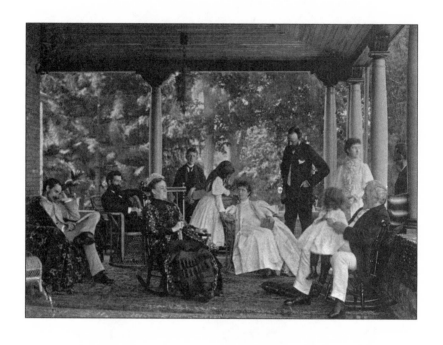

Trask family and friends on the porch of the first
Yaddo, circa 1886. From left to right: Henry van Dyke,
George Foster Peabody, Kate's mother Christina Nichols in
rocking chair, Kate's young brother Acosta, Christina, Kate,
and Spencer at center, the children's tutor Allena Pardee,
and noted painter and photographer Eastman Johnson,
holding young Junius on his lap.

{ Courtesy Saratoga Springs History Museum }

Chapter Two

The Inspiration

"I explain it to myself as a natural psychic phenomenon."[18] If we can receive wireless messages from across the ocean, why can we not receive messages from Above? From the time of my youth I have experienced dazzling though brief moments of truth, sudden visions or premonitions opening to me like the sun as it might suddenly appear from behind a cloud on an overcast day. Mother always remarked that Kate has a rich inner life, that I was a child adrift in my own world of books and the imaginings they inspired. Perhaps I am that melodramatic dreamer, but I have had real visions. I have had epiphanies which miraculously appear at junctures and crossroads in my life just in time to inform my choices. So on this brilliant summer day in 1899 as Spencer and I took our usual walk, the unfolding event was really not so surprising, at least to me. We were strolling along a path at Yaddo through the woods and then onto the open road up to the Stone Tower. Spencer had fallen behind me, gazing up at an azure sky and glistening leaves after a lovely morning shower, and I had walked ahead to see a patch of white wildflowers.

"Suddenly! an unseen hand seemed laid upon me,

*an unheard voice seemed calling to me. I stopped short —
I felt as if Something, which I could not see, stood in my
path: I believe my hands rose before me, outstretched, as if
in appeal to that Something which was too vast for me to
define."* [19]

Spencer called out to me. What could be the matter? Was I all right?

And then I spoke: it was as though some spirit
other than my own were speaking through me.

*"At last, I know, at last I understand," I said, "The
thing men say they feel at Yaddo is not what IS — it is
what IS TO BE. Yaddo is not to be an institution, a school, a
charity. It is to be always a place of inspiration, a delightful,
hospitable home where guests may come and find welcome.
Here will be a perpetual series of house parties — of literary
men, literary women, and other artists. Those who are city-
weary, who are thirsting for the country and for beauty,
who are hemmed in by circumstance and have no opportunity to make for themselves an harmonious environment,
shall seek it here. At Yaddo they will find the Sacred Fire,
and light their torches in the flame. Look, Spencer! They
are walking in the woods, wandering in the garden, sitting
under the pine trees — creating, creating, creating."* [20]

And I turned around to find Spencer, struck still,
as if in a trance himself. Slowly he spoke, and he too saw
what I saw and heard what I heard, and there, now hand
in hand, we saw so clearly what our legacy would be. For
years we had struggled with the idea of how to bequeath
our beautiful sanctuary Yaddo... not to family, they had
no need, not to friends, they had their estates, not as a
school, or a hospital. But what of a gift of Yaddo as a liv-

ing, continuing offering to creative people?

Suddenly there in the woods we sat down together on a bed of wildflowers and planned like two small children hatching the most marvelous secret plan our whole concept for Yaddo. "Pine Garde" it shall be, I had suggested, and we agreed that the idea of our artists' retreat would be a closely guarded secret until after our deaths.

"Pine Garde, my darling, named after you. Do you remember the skit last year, when you were costumed as the pine tree, ever tall, strong, protective? Spencer Trask, armored in pine cones and branches holding the sapling as a staff? Symbolizing strength? A double-meaning, too, I think, because it showed your own inward character. Staunchness."

He kissed me excitedly and pulled me up to do a whirl-around before we settled back on the ground to organize more delicious details.

I watched my husband's hands flying about excitedly as ideas came tumbling down upon him and he began envisioning our Yaddo as all it could be for the future. First, he said, a corporation should be formed right away, our Pine Garde, with the governing board comprised of our trusted "inner circle": Foster, our attorney Edward Shepard, Bishop Doane in Albany, Henry van Dyke, my childhood friend… and Alenna, I shouted. It was settled. We would all meet this winter in Brooklyn at Foster's home. Later that night we began to formulate the words for our vision; we phrased and re-phrased the mission of Yaddo and finally decided on this:

"We desire to found here a permanent home to which may come from time to time for rest and refreshment

authors, painters, sculptors, musicians, and other artists both men and women few in number and chosen for creative gifts and besides and not less for the power and the purpose to make these gifts useful to the world."[21]

The board of Yaddo, with help from their artistic and intellectual friends and connections, would issue the invitations to the artists. They would select the most creative candidates, and see that Yaddo's hospitality, quietude and inspiration would nurture the guests and enable their creativity. Yaddo would protect culture for the future, freeing artists from the exigencies of making a living. It was for Spencer and me our *unique* mission, our sacred gift to the future of American — no, world — culture.

Having thought through the workings of the board, we next began to think of the estate itself and how it should be readied for its secret destiny. Spencer was exuberant. Suddenly he could orchestrate grand plans for outbuildings, for gardens. All of Yaddo estate suddenly took on a larger meaning, a loftier joy, and an unfolding hope which we had lost since our children were taken.[22] No more would we think of Yaddo "as a place that had failed of its ultimate destiny, because now this sacred place which had inspired so many, ourselves included, would go on and on, only gaining in beauty and inspiration."[23] Now we would live again with purpose. The beautiful Hebe statue in the entrance to our Great Hall, goddess of Youth and Springtime, now no longer seemed a hollow promise to the Trasks. There would always be at Yaddo the promise of re-birth and creation, long after Spencer and I were laid to rest.

That summer was one of high purpose for Spencer as he planned our garden, the "Poet's Corner of Yaddo," a birthday gift to me, and far better than jewelry or another sea voyage. The space would be formal to offset the random natural design of the surrounding woods, but it also would include areas of Romantic wildness. The result: a delightful garden which mixed the hand of man with Nature. At the foot of the hill running down from the mansion house would be a pool with fountains and a playful cherub wakening two water nymphs who lived among water lilies. Whimsy and delight would be my first morning view from the tower window!

During those early days of planning, I stood at the window watching Spencer, tall and elegant on his horse surveying the area, stopping occasionally to look up at a cloud formation or to take in the fresh smell of pine. He came to my room like a jubilant young boy with his ideas for the rose plantings — red, pink, white, and cheerful yellow — and I dropped everything, catching the moment of celebration, to walk on his arm about the planned area. We were two happy children. I stressed to Spencer what I did NOT want: a "garden where botanical enthusiasts vie with each other in remembering names that they cannot pronounce." [24] No ticketing and Latin names here. I will not "bound delight with labels and small sticks," I insisted.

Spencer laid out the entire garden, with its long straight rows of roses meeting at a circular fountain in the middle, a fountain inhabited by brightly-colored Japanese fish. [25] We wanted all the gardens to be an expression of Love and Nature; and because we both admired the classicism of Greece in the ruins of southern Italy and Sicily, we wanted statuary of gods and goddesses. Four classic marble nymphs behind the pool celebrated the seasons, holding pinecones for winter, flowers for spring, fruit for summer, wheat sheaves for autumn. From the pool, marble steps would lead up to an imposing terrace, Italian pots such as those found on the porches of villas hanging over the Tyrrhenian Sea at each level. Foster shared the excitement over our vision for Yaddo's future and on my birthday, the thirtieth of May, we received a letter from him instructing Spencer to purchase some statuary for the steps as a birthday gift from him.[26] His touch and his taste were everywhere in our home, and so matching our own inclinations. Spencer envisioned a sundial for the center of the terrace. After considerable research, Spencer had ours made in England; it was placed on a base copied from a table excavated from Pompeii's ruins which we had seen on our visit to Naples. "Katrina's Sun-Dial," as it came to be called, had inscribed on it the words of our friend the poet Henry van Dyke, written to me as a most flattering tribute. It read:

    "Hours fly,
    Flowers die.
    New days,
    New ways,
    Pass by.
    Love stays."

— while on the base was written:

Time is
Too Slow for those who Wait,
Too Swift for those who Fear,
Too Long for those who Grieve,
Too Short for those who Rejoice;
But for those who Love,
Time is Eternity." [27]

As garden plans came along various friends suggested some "must include" ideas — those in-vogue Italian satyrs and other frightful creatures, or a sundial with words from the Medicis — but we smiled and made the space express our own ideals and those of Yaddo. Sunny Italy with its classicism and symmetry would become part of our American idyll, but not all of it. Our garden would not be distinctly Italian, French, or English, but a happy mixing of all the elements which reflected us. "No Medici family with its blood-stained race to come between us and the sun," [28] I had emphasized. Not on *our* sundial.

The terrace was later covered by a columned pergola extending the whole length where rambling roses would grow. Later, too, came a surprise: a classical, porticoed gateway entrance to the garden from the mansion, a gateway Spencer personally had designed for me. I would enter my garden between marble columns and beneath these words from my husband: "*Spencer Trask laid out this rose garden in honor of his wife Katrina, author, poet, woman. Go happy rose and enterwove with other flowers, bind my love. 1899.*"

Beyond the pergola Spencer thought of using the

dolomite rocks from our quarry to form two levels of gardens with a little stream joyfully skipping its way down, around, through shady areas of hosta and astilbe and woodland "volunteers." The rock garden was a "fascinating, delicious aside" from the more ordered spaces in our garden plan. Whenever I sat there in the shade listening to the sound of rippling water and the splash of the fountains in the lotus-filled pools, I felt a wonderful presence, mysterious and inspirational.[29] We hoped the various styles of gardens and the meandering pathways would encourage pleasant strolling and peaceful reflection for our Yaddo guests, too. A garden is meant to be shared.

Off from the rose garden to the east in a grove of pines we would place later the white marble statue of the young knight Cristalan, wreathed at the base in myrtle, as a loving memorial to our four children. I had anonymously published a long poem in 1893 entitled *Under King Constantine,* and the chivalrous and pure knight Cristalan for me represented the ideal tribute to our four little ones sleeping in the Greenwood Cemetery in Brooklyn. Now the children would be a part of this second Yaddo, and though their voices never had filled the halls here, though they had never played in this garden, the statue would bring me a sense of our larger family as it might have been. My friend Ordway Partridge the sculptor had perfectly captured the aspirations and dreams of youth in the marble boy looking upward from its base of myrtle, the white form symbolizing victory over mortality.

I must pause now, for suddenly, as I share this story with you, I am overcome with waves of sorrow and grieving for my lost children. Staggering to the stone bench I sit down. Sorrow knots my throat. Here sits a woman who once held a golden-haired boy who gave candy kisses and protected butterflies and sent valiant tin soldiers "into the Valley of Death." How persistent grief is! Having put it safely aside, having not seen its face for weeks, or months, buried it securely beneath the bustle of activity, it reappears, triggered by some memory or thought. Here on this stone bench in my garden I remember my boy Junius at five. I remember his most earnest question: *"God is very good to give Junius his pretty house, but who gives that little poor boy his nasty house?"*[30] I picture his large eyes looking up at me when I asked him to tell me just HOW much he loved his mama, and he said, *"Oh Mama, me don't talk about it, me just do it."*[31]

I have the great inclination to go, now, to my tower room and open the top drawer. Here is where I keep my treasures, the childhood mementoes kept safely in Brooklyn, now brought here to be near me. The tin soldiers, the little toy sheep, the drawing pens, the Marie Antoinette costume. Here I have put away the things left to me in Christina's will, long before she would become an angel. *"To my mother I leave my Bible, my prayer-book, and my locked book."*[32] Christina, named for my noble saintly mother, now gone from me as well. Christina, who rode the spotted pony oh so fast, who climbed the apple tree way too high, who brought me violets between two parchment cards tied in blue ribbon. My wise reader of Marcus Aurelius who took his words to her heart and decided not "to get even" with a naughty boy in her little social world, but *"to punish the wrong-doer by not becoming like him."*

"And so, Mama, I merely walked away."[33]

Here beside the statue of Christalan I weep, so remembering. Sitting on the poet's bench I weep and remember.

"Silent stood Christalan
And faced their coming, not a trace of fear
Or tremor in his bearing, slight and frail
In his white doublet, holding in his hand
The white lilies he forgot to drop."

You all have lied who told me time would ease this pain.

"Sir Christalan, the Valiant and the True;
God speed the soul of our beloved knight,
Sir Christalan, the Valiant and the True."[34] ❀

Statue of Christalan by William
Ordway Partridge, 1900, in the Yaddo Gardens.
{ Photo by the author }

Yaddo Gardens designed by Spencer
Trask, a mixture of the formal and the poetic.

Above: Katrina's porticoed entrance to her gardens
reads, in part, "Katrina / Author Poet Woman."

Opposite: Views of the pergola and sun-dial,
which look east toward Vermont.

{ Gustave Lorey photographs, courtesy of Jane Wait }

The Grand Union Hotel, circa 1890.
{ Courtesy Saratoga Springs History Museum }

Chapter Three

Summer Colonies and Friends Who Mattered

August in Saratoga Springs at the turn of the century was a spectacle: the name Gay Nineties applied more to our summer town than any other place I could imagine. More and more wealthy, carefree, exuberant summer visitors came each year, swelling the sleepy village population and bringing in a million dollars a day just from expenditures at hotels, boarding houses, restaurants, and the springs — twice that was spent in the gaming houses.[35] There was a frenzy of buying along Broadway in the new retail boutiques; a buzz of voices at the mineral springs' bath houses in the mornings and afternoons; a parade of splendidly-attired guests at the big hotels; and laughter emanating from the Queen Anne-style summer cottages of upper Broadway and along Union Avenue where repeat summer guests now had built their own mansions. Storefronts displayed flower boxes, carriages were equipped as grandly as their meticulously-attired drivers, and now a few of the new autos vied for control of Broadway.

Visitors in extravagant attire with rolls of green bills and nothing but leisure time crowded the racetrack and then continued their gains or losses in Congress Park.[36] Richard Canfield, the gaming magnate from New York city, had bought and renovated the old Morrissey Club House and turned it into the sumptuous and elegant Canfield Casino where the finest food and drink were served at the finest prices. Patrons played in evening clothes and wore costly jewelry; the Casino extended credit and hired guards to protect the finery of the eager clientele while they enjoyed its temptations.[37] The Canfield Casino and other gambling houses about the city were so successful that gambling became the main draw for summer visitors — but it also attracted the critics to Saratoga. In 1894 Joseph Pulitzer of the *New York World* sent his most famous reporter known as Nellie Bly to Saratoga to report on the evils of the summer resort. She regaled her readers with tales of "wickedness, dissipation, and profligacy at this once most respectable watering-place."[38]

As I mentioned earlier, Anthony Comstock also came up from New York, bringing his crusade. He was the rather unattractive self-appointed moralist and secretary of the New York Society for the Suppression of Vice, and he arrived armed with outrage, and held meetings to try to close down the gambling houses. Spencer went to the meetings, holding the man, as he said, "at arms length," because basically he "was not our sort" — but nevertheless we signed his petition. Spencer agreed with Comstock's assessment of the evils of gambling, and worked assiduously to rid the city of it, but the efforts came to short-lived success. The gaming houses closed down, then reopened when Comstock left town.

We personally sent in hired detectives from New York, but when offenders were jailed, they were soon free on bail and back in the gambling houses. Spencer thought the casinos were ruining Saratoga's true gifts as a summer resort; but his struggle was hopeless against a tidal wave of revelry, endless money, increasing gambling enthusiasts, and a happy town reaping the financial benefits while turning a blind eye.[39]

If I must give credit at all to Mr. Canfield, it would be my admiration for a man who taught himself, from a jail cell in the beginning, the love of books, of art, of fine furnishings. Richard Canfield found in the collecting of these objects of beauty more pleasure than the accumulation of money for its own sake.[40] I secretly longed to see his painting collection.

There were concerts in the park and concerts at the grand hotels, with popular conductors like John Philip Sousa and Victor Herbert and famed singers like the great Caruso and the Irish tenor Chauncey Olcott. It was reported that a flamboyant young man named Florenz Ziegfeld was a regular at the gaming tables with his Paris dance-hall companion Anna Held — and that she actually "bathed in milk for her complexion."[41] Our rather gossipy head gardener had filled me in with this tidbit. During their leisure time, our household staff loved the fireworks after dark, the Punch and Judy show, and taking in the parade of smartly dressed visitors. Next day in the kitchen or in the garden or the barns they would report in great detail on the Saratoga comedy of manners seen and heard on an excursion "down town."

The Grand Union was the largest of the hotels, with 824 guest rooms, but others quickly appeared to accommodate the growing crowds of summer. It was refurbished in the 1870s by the "department store" Mr. Stewart from New York, and took up seven acres in the heart of Saratoga, facing Broadway and with wings nearly a quarter-of-a-mile long enclosing tree-shaded gardens. It had a dining room serving over a thousand guests at a seating, and was equipped with marble floors, carved walnut furniture, Otis elevators, electric chandeliers, and a meat locker in the cellar packed with meats from most of Saratoga's sheep and cattle farms, slaughtered in time for season. Its floor-to-ceiling ballroom painting was famous, "the young America, depicted as a lush maiden," generously giving her bounty to the whole world.[42]

Most summer visitors to Saratoga were unable to break the exclusive social barriers of Newport and chose the more accepting, open society found in the Spa City. One such regular visitor was James Brady, the colorful "Diamond Jim" often seen in town with the actress Lillian Russell, the two of them making news daily either in New York or Saratoga, creating excitement and curiosity with their bicycle built for two, his enormous girth, and their mutual appetite for food and jewelry and high living. Jim Brady could be sighted in New York at all the Broadway openings, at the fights of John L. Sullivan, in the Manhattan lobster palaces, in the finest hotel dining rooms, and at the racetrack following his horses. Reporters hovered for a story, and a band of followers was always near hoping to cash in on Diamond

Jim's widely-known generosity.

Must I admit I read New York's *Town Tattler?* Yes I do, if only to marvel at the outrageous choices and shallow lives of most of New York society. And yes, I do, despite Spencer's personal connection to the *New York Times,* the paper he had rescued from bankruptcy some years earlier. It was the respected read of the businessman, the intellectual, the financier. Yes, the *Times* did report on social events with verve. But the gossipy, primary-focus "society news" in New York undoubtedly was in the *Tattler,* where the extravagant social activities, lavish spending, and "delicious" misbehavior of the wealthy were outlined in barely-veiled reference. The scandals of the Vanderbilts and the Belmonts, the arranged marriages of rich American daughters to impoverished titled foreigners, the costly costume balls of Caroline Astor were of great interest not only to the subjects of the gossipy reporting, but to the "inquiring" public in general.

Most of the newspapers also were full of Diamond Jim Brady stories, but he was not invited to the private society fetes, balls, and debutante parties, despite his millions. He was excluded from Newport in August, but he was a welcomed visitor to a more democratic-minded Saratoga Springs in the late days of summer. Diamond Jim was known not only for the twinkle in his Irish eyes, for his bombastic and charismatic personality, but for his open-hearted philanthropy, even if the source of his millions from the railroads was "at question." I do not judge. After all, wasn't the business of railroads in some fashion responsible for much of our own wealth...

and that of Foster's? And would I condemn the elder Mr. Rockefeller as ruthless creator of monopolies, when also he was creator of universities, museums, hospitals and research institutions which were eradicating dread diseases like hook-worm, yellow fever?

Truth be known, I couldn't help feeling joy for such a character as Jim Brady with his obvious sense of caring for others. None of his business practices harmed people: trading "special information" stories and acting on "advance details" of businesses was *commonplace* these days, an accepted occurrence at the men's city clubs after hours over cigars. Secretly I rather enjoyed the reports of Diamond Jim's "shenanigans" in New York or at Saratoga. Oddly, when it came to Brady, I just mentally isolated and set aside the gambling aspects of his life, even though Spencer was ever campaigning against the practice.

One had to love the *lack of social pretense*, the true Irish character in this larger-than-life man. I certainly loved James Buchanan Brady, and my Irish household staff loved that I loved him. His clever rise from poverty in the tenements through keen observation of opportunity and pure salesmanship. His unmatched optimism. His open pocketbook for the elevator boy, the taxi driver, the stranded show-girl, a hospital in need, a down-and-out acquaintance.[43] His self-deprecation and self-knowledge, his infectious physical energy, his endurance through unrequited loves and his great belly-laugh at Life when it conspired to bring him down. I applauded *all* that in him.

Yes, downtown Saratoga WAS electric with energy

from all kinds of people and all classes and I dare say representative of the new kind of America. In the meantime, it was left to us, perhaps the Old Guard, those who had inherited artistic and creative sensibilities, and intellectual "history" you might say, to champion the arts, music, literature, philosophy. Spencer in particular was actively supporting the arts societies and museums in New York, through his innate sense of propriety and harmony in design... and also through financial support and his ability to socially connect other generous-minded friends to his cause. I did my part by bringing creative people to our home for lectures, performances, readings, and concerts and offering them to our friends and guests. We saw ourselves as custodians of culture. There was always good conversation. Sparks of creativity lighted our salons: we strived for enlightenment and improvement, not mere entertainment. There was no ballroom at Yaddo.

In the latter years of the nineteenth century, American society was run by us women. The household was defined and directed by women: we set the tone, established the mores and customs, championed good taste and manners. The men had left it to us: they were occupied with creating the wealth for the family or for their business. The social direction of America lay in the hands of women, and in particular those of us with wealth and established position. Personally I was striving to champion all these acceptable customs and codes of behavior at Yaddo, as I had been taught: decorum, good taste and good judgment, discretion, humility, woman as able director of the family household. But I also felt our particular age had some real fault lines. I found myself sometimes casting a critical eye on my historical time, its people, their life and choices, sensing there were tremors in our social world, transition and change cracking through the crust. There were old practices and views which suddenly were appearing clearly wrong, unacceptable. Some of the Old Rules seemed now bigoted, exclusionary, rigid.

I found myself beginning to pay attention to a *different* kind of person I saw around me, a new social type lacking the old trappings of acceptability, but exhibiting admirable traits of compassion and generosity, hard work and mental discipline. And the "new Americans" were descending on Saratoga. I found myself more and more distressed by the attitudes and behavior of some of our *privileged* friends and acquaintances and business associates. Spencer and I staunchly championed culture and art and propriety and felt no restraints in enjoying the benefits of our wealth, position, and class. I straightened the sapphire ring on my finger, adjusted the Worth jacket with its jet buttons and walked into church proudly with self-assurance. I was the esteemed Mrs. Spencer Trask, but there was a gnawing feeling in my stomach.

Within I felt a restlessness. What more should I be doing? I knew we were leaving a legacy for the cultural world with our posthumous gift of Yaddo. But now, during my lifetime, with all my wealth and talents and material gifts, what should I choose as my practical mission in this changing world? The reliable answer was that my ill health restricted me. The status quo for

Mrs. Trask remained so because of her heart condition; she was limited in her response to any "call." I reassured myself that the world could never say the Trasks did not value service to others and that we did not give generously. I had no censure from the world, only from myself.

Many friends of ours from New York and Philadelphia of late had chosen to join a different summer colony from our Saratoga Springs. This summer colony was gathering along the western shores of beautiful Lake George, just a few miles farther north. Some wealthy families went even *farther* north and west into the Adirondack wilderness to build large rustic chalets on Saranac or Raquette Lake or by a trout stream. These "camps" were built of native materials, simple logs and rock, finished and adorned with limbs, twigs, bark. But the interiors boasted Oriental rugs, Turkish fabric on cushions, exotic hunting trophies, bowling allies, and sideboards laden with Bavarian china and bone-handled silver. The summer guests and their elaborate entourage came by private railroad car from New York to the Adirondacks, and then boarded coaches or steamers to their private lake properties or hotels.

Other families of means had discovered the summer glory of the rolling Berkshires around Stockbridge and Lenox, or the rocky shores of Maine. And the *most* socially exclusive families had staked out private enclaves in Newport and erected marble mansions in the formal Beaux-Arts style along Bellevue Avenue or Cliff Walk on the Atlantic.

We had followed Spencer's father in choosing Saratoga Springs for our seasonal country home, and I was happy to be in the lovely wilderness of our estate which was easily reached by train from the city. Here, Spencer's business demands and commitments in New York were well accommodated. I relished the peacefulness of Yaddo and mostly avoided the physically-challenging bustle of down-town Saratoga except for church services and activities which supported our local philanthropies. I did take interest in Lucy Skidmore Scribner's new Young Women's Industrial Club off Union Avenue, however. This local institution had been founded in 1903 by five bright Saratoga women along with Mrs. Scribner, the publishing heiress, as a practical training school for young women, with the dream that it would evolve into a full-fledged women's college. I would live to see its dream come true in 1911.

I enjoyed people and fun as much as the next lady, but my personal preference was for the solitary serenity of Yaddo. Quietly from my woodland paradise I contributed in my own way to the good life in Saratoga by opening Yaddo for civic endeavors and cultural events and by charity for the hospital and school we had established.

My husband's nature always puzzled and delighted me. He was able to merge his Puritan seriousness with extravagant showmanship and *joie de vivre* in his own life. I believe the latter side came from his French Huguenot mother's lineage.[44] He loved his possessions, his play-things, the royal friends and talented artistic connections on his social calendar, the extravagant dinners he hosted for various foreign and national notables in a New York restaurant or at one of his private men's clubs. He savored the quite opulent personal apartment he built at the top of his Bowling Green offices at numbers nine-to-eleven Broadway, an apartment boasting African mahogany and carved oak, gleaming bathrooms, Belgian tapestries, fine paintings, Persian rugs, and liveried attendants.[45] But in his pocket always was the note on covetousness, the warning of putting too much value on material things.

I always sensed his inward struggle between Puritan simplicity and humility and his avid appreciation and collection of things aesthetically pleasing. He admired things that were beautiful, there was no doubt. But he had a project into which he poured supreme, directed, *serious* energy, a project in which the "beautiful thing" was actually our adopted city: Saratoga Springs. For years he made it his mission to make Saratoga a spa city equal to the great European health centers such as Baden Baden. Curtailing gambling was one imperative; the other was protecting the mineral springs themselves from over-commercialization and manipulation by local bottlers. It would be his grand cause for which he expended time and money. Later it would cost him his life.

Spencer and I had nothing against the race course next to us — it was in place before we bought our property — but we preferred the beauty of the horses and the pageantry of racing without the gambling aspect. Protesting the wagering there was to no avail, as we discovered. But occasionally we had to ask the male employees of the track not to bathe in our lakes as it was quite unseemly for our household staff. Basically we at Yaddo co-existed pleasantly next to the increasingly-popular venue. We had vast acreage as a buffer from the noise and summer activity.

My family and Spencer's family visited us frequently, and we took joy in our nieces and nephews and the sound of children having summer fun. In the tradition of Spencer's father we, too, became involved in the annual Flower Fête, in which flower-bedecked carriages, floats, and bicycles paraded down Broadway. The event rivaled similar festivals in Nice and Cannes and New Orleans and received much publicity, even down in New York.[46] I cherish this image of my husband: jaunty straw hat and white linen suit, his buggy a sunny shade of yellow from its cape of chrysanthemums and dahlias, his horse swathed in yellow roses... and the *New York Times* acknowledgment that none could outdo the splendor of Spencer Trask at this summer's Flower Fête.

Foster was one of our most frequent guests at Yaddo, not a guest, really, but part of our family. *"How proud of you I am, my Wise Counselor,"* I often told him. His noble efforts for education, when he had been forced by parental poverty to educate himself at the Y. M. C. A. in Brooklyn, were so remarkable. No other autodidact achieved such accolades in the educational world as Foster. His rapacious reading and constant study as a young man to achieve his *self*-education could be measured against Spencer's entitled and traditional one at Princeton, and both now sifted out as the same pure gold.

"I shall now have to call you Doctor," I said with a loving kiss. He had been awarded an honorary Master of Arts degree by Harvard University, and the Harvard President, in his address, referred to Peabody as "wise counselor." He had also been given a LLD by Washington and Lee University and a Doctor of Laws by the University of Georgia.[47]

His self-acquired personal wealth had been almost as great as Spencer's, and when he was not out West on business for Spencer Trask and Company he, too, enjoyed a summer home in the country. Foster had fallen in love with Lake George, some thirty miles north of Saratoga Springs, a beautiful spring-fed, thirty-two-mile lake cradled by mountains of granite and woods. The Queen of American Lakes was blessed with small picturesque, forested islands strewn like jewels in the clear, cool waters. Boats and steam yachts with portable wicker chairs could come from the shores into the snug harbors of the islands and bring picnickers with parasols and hampers. There happy groups could sit on the rocks or on their chairs on the mossy shores and admire a many-layered horizon of mountain peaks.

I had spent some family summers there as a dreamy young adolescent with a rich inner life of poetry and secret promises for the future. Thomas Jefferson had hailed Lake George as "the most beautiful lake in the New World." There were few tourists and vast acres of pristine shoreline running from Caldwell Village northward, almost to Lake Champlain. Foster had purchased hundreds of acres on the west shore of the lake which included the old Colonel Price home. He had invested much creative energy and wealth into its refurbishment and embellishment and named his summer home Abenia: we both had a special love of local Indian lore, and he chose this name from an Algonquin Indian word meaning "Home of Rest." His brothers Royal and Charles J. Peabody also purchased land on the lake and built handsome villas with commanding views, and his good friend (and ours) Edward Morse Shepard had built his lovely Erlowest on nearby property.

I cherished traveling up for weekends at Abenia. Foster's many guests were always varied and stimulating, his furniture and art were in great taste, and I loved sitting in the rocker on his front porch, luxuriating in the long views. Here along "Millionaire's Row" on the west side residents stayed on or about the water, and were not so involved in a city, like the residents of Saratoga Springs. It was a rural life, with mostly home entertainment, teas and dinner parties, and sports like golf, tennis, power-boating, and billiards. On my visits I enjoyed the dinner parties and the conversations, the gardens and greenhouse, the myriad of animal skin rugs from the West inviting a bare foot in the parlor — but most of all, I loved the lake.

Fatigue, chest pains, all were dispelled when I heard the sound of the water on the rocks. My heart leaped to see the color changes on the surface of the lake as the sun rose orange, then brilliant pink. In the afternoons, I relished the view of Buck Mountain caught in the setting sun's rays, and the sight of the *Minne-ha-ha* tourist boat steaming northward from its village berth. It glided through the lake waters below, past us summer folks up on the Abenia porch or in the rose garden, and the voice of the boat captain carried over the water, mentioning names like Peabody, Shepard, Tuttle to entertain the tourists on board. The *Minne-ha-ha* enjoyed a bustling business from hotel guests in the village, all eager to see the new mansions appearing along the shores and to hear stories about the wealthy or famous owners.

About this time, other titans of business and finance, opera singers, wealthy owners of power boats, artists and titled foreigners were also discovering the allure of Lake George in the summer and were acquiring property further north in the shore village called Bolton Landing. Many of the moneyed and famous players of the Gilded Age... they were calling it this thanks to a book by Mark Twain... came to Lake George, bought properties, built their dream estates, and set about entertaining each other. Many were reclusive, but others sought to keep up with or perhaps out-do their fellow summer people in their lake mansions, their interior decorations, and their racing yachts. The majority were independent-minded successful businessmen who had garnered great wealth through keen insight, daring risks, and an indomitable work ethic. They were often curious learners and travelers, some avid collectors, generous givers... all adventuresome individuals with widespread interests and talents.

If Foster Peabody was the debonair entertainer and his Abenia parties the favored social invitation, the Spencer Trasks were hosts to numerous and intimate "evenings at home" at Yaddo. We liked to feature chamber music, chorales, lectures, or poetry reading before dinner, and I particularly enjoyed arranging my hand-painted place-cards just so, insuring that dynamic but decorous conversations resulted among the varied guests. In moments of perversity I would place the liberal next to the conservative, the strait-laced with the libertine, and watch demurely the fireworks of sputtering and the rising of color in cheeks. I so love debate, the dialectic, ideas filling the room, and challenging philosophies taking firm but friendly battle positions. We invited politicians, financiers, sculptors, artists and publishers, friends from abroad, and family friends. We all felt we were living in a dynamic, progressive time period on the cusp of change, and there was much to discuss. But the rule was "discretion" in conversation, and kindliness.

Neither Spencer nor I were "prohibitionists." To be sure, wine did flow quite freely at Yaddo, but Spencer did not like the taste of it and I felt the Saratoga water was restorative for me. A specialty on our table was our own Yaddo ice, from our clear spring water on the property, harvested and stored in the Gothic-style Stone Tower. I used it as table decoration, the ice sparkling like diamonds in the crystal bowls by candlelight. I softened the effect with pink roses in the Tiffany silver vases. (Kudos, I must add, to Tiffany's in New York... their people were ever filling my orders for engraved vases of

silver, the favorite gift of thanks for others' kindnesses.)
Our Yaddo toasts were a tradition:

May your mind ever be as clear,
May your heart ever be as fresh,
May your soul ever be as pure
As this water. [48]

I really thought not too much about the food
served at Yaddo, or the menus... except when guests
had particular allergies or there was someone from
abroad who might want a "typical American dinner." I
do chuckle when I think of one dinner when we entertained the little girls of St. Christina's with Sister Mary.
I wrote in my journal that those hungry little ladies
found "legends in the turkey, poetry in the pies, and
idylls in the ice-cream." Spencer said these home feasts
for the homeless were "like wild flowers in the midst
of orchids" and we laughed when several of the girls
suddenly stood up and jumped up and down merrily,
"shaking it down" they said, to "make room for more
mince pie and Christmas pudding."[49]

I'm now remembering one dinner when we had
some English guests hotly discussing "the Irish question." I was told to be umpire. And to be silent. These
lawyers debated their impressions of Gladstone, where-
upon I (being "at heart" Irish) HAD to take part, being a
woman of OPINIONS. I later learned the servants were
leaning ears against the door to the dining room, cheer-
ing me on silently, delighted that I perhaps did have
Irish blood in my veins, and stating that "Mrs. Trask
gave them English the old one-two, I say."[50]

Sometimes I *did* get surprises, foreign guests who came to us with letters from various friends, stating that Spencer and I would enjoy their viewpoints and insights, or that we would be doing our *friends* a great deed by entertaining certain of these guests. One evening we entertained a delightful Japanese man who afterwards wrote our friends that never had he "enjoyed so many fine ladies at one time," and that he had entered the Trask dining room "in the arms of Mrs. Trask herself."[51]

One of our caveats among our friends who came to dinner was that we should be kind about discussing people, and that all dinner topics should be debated vigorously but not in a mean-spirited or personally offensive way. Almost always, of course, ladies and gentlemen arrived with their set prejudices, but it was hoped they would discuss matters decorously. One night a dinner guest, a comparative stranger, sat on my right. Midway through dinner as we discussed the European war and our relation to it, he announced in a loud voice that all Pacifists should be shot. (This knowing I was a pacifist.) I calmly requested if we might not wait until after coffee and dessert were served "so that I might have strength to face the ordeal." He pulled himself up by his short little neck and replied that I "was only adding flippancy to treason."[52] I was aghast when the guest on my left AGREED with him. (So that evening Mrs. Trask was riddled with shot!!)[53]

Tonight there were fourteen guests for dinner at Yaddo, a group Foster had brought together for a "cause dear to his heart." We always began the evenings with refreshment, typically Saratoga spring water and cheese and mushroom canapés in the drawing room. On this night the erect and immaculately-dressed Mr. Booker T. Washington stood out among our other guests. I had welcomed the idea of entertaining this Negro educator at Yaddo on one of his trips north, and knew Foster had been a benefactor to his Negro institute in Alabama. I had read his book *Up From Slavery* and in fact had solidified some of my own views after reading his words. It would be exciting to have as a dinner guest someone who "came up from slavery" and who became the first Negro to receive an honorary PhD degree from Harvard and to be invited to the White House.

We met in the front parlor and he complimented the crystalline water, always offered in beautiful glasses and apparently enjoyed as much as wine or other alcohol. He was fair in color for his race: his father had been a white farmer and his mother a slave. His book *Up From Slavery* had been recently serialized and he was considered to be more "reasonable and practical" than the other notable Negro ("firebrand"?) of the time, Mr. W. E. B. DuBois. As Mr. Washington talked, my soul was stirred, and I felt in *closer* touch with our great racial problem since the Civil War, the problems of reconstructing the south and educating the newly-freed slaves. He spoke so simply, so humbly of his life. He was born a slave, and with absolute freedom from pride in all his many accomplishments, he made me realize the possibilities — oh the *possibilities* — of bettering the lot of the Negro through education and economic opportunity and training.

Mr. Washington obviously was taken with the

beauty of Yaddo. He admired Mr. Eastman Johnson's portraits of our Junius and Christina, and showed a high intellect and appreciation of the arts for a man born in a slave cabin. He had read some of my essays and complimented me.

"Mrs. Trask, I admire your philosophy in the treatment of your household staff. From the beginning at Tuskegee my students built their own quarters. I wanted them to see the beauty and dignity of their labor. I wanted them to lift their toil up from mere drudgery and see pride in their work. I aim to educate hand AND head. We must be practical in our lives, Mrs. Trask."[54]

"Mr. Washington, as you know, your work and your philosophy are greatly admired by my friend Mr. Peabody. I want to assure you that Mr. Trask and I, too, plan to contribute to your Institute."

"You are most kind, and I appreciate your hospitality when you are aware that my sole purpose for coming North is to seek funds and support. I hesitate to take your fine hospitality to enlighten you of my life's work. My life's work, however, DEPENDS on the wealthy like you and Mr. Trask, and of course Mr. Peabody, who give so greatly to charities. I have no patience with criticisms of the rich, because they are rich. They serve a noble purpose for mankind, in their accomplishments and in their providing employment and opportunities for the masses."[55]

"Yes, I believe that is so, and we in turn must..."

"How many people would be made poor if suddenly the rich gave a large proportion of their wealth to charity. Why business would be disrupted and American enterprises would grind to a halt without the 'oil' of the rich. It is *surprising how generous most American rich ARE."* [56] The whites of his eyes grew wider as he spoke, and he sat taller in the engulfing dining room chair which held his tidy small frame in its neat suit.

"I do not believe you are here to beg, Mr. Washington, but simply to enjoy the beauty of Yaddo and to enjoy our company. It is we who are blessed with your visit. You have my utmost admiration, sir."

Mr. Washington's eyes twinkled. With a burst of genius and courage he continued.

"I have usually proceeded on the principle that persons who possess enough sense to earn money usually have sense enough to know how to give it away." [57]

I smiled warmly at my dinner guest, and touched his arm.

"And you and I agree that making others happy and productive is a true goal."

"And Mrs. Trask, the HAPPIEST people are those that do the most for others." [58]

Spencer leaned from across the table having heard our conversation. He always heard *all* the conversations, and digested them perfectly while lending the perfect ear to his dinner partner.

"My wife is more socialistic than I, Mr. Washington. She often despairs over the wide breach between the haves and the have-nots, the rich and the poor. I am a sympathetic and generous man, but I do not cringe at the idea that I possess many estates, have accumulated great wealth. By the hardest work of my mind, by self-denial and deep concentration I have been successful in my profession, and I am not at all troubled to own a number of estates. There

are economic REASONS for the centuries-old differences in wealth among men. My duty is to run my business honorably, and treat my fellow man fairly. The integrity of my character is what is important, not whether I am rich or poor."

I gently interrupted my husband as my eyes signaled for Betty to present the cobbler, the luscious blackberries having come from our garden at Yaddo. We then ventured perhaps more safely into talk of sugar beets and sweet potatoes, and the personal story of Mr. Washington's visit to the White House. The conversation now rushed along, like a brook, happily. Foster's eyes met mine. He was delighted to have me meet his friend. Mr. Washington's cause was a special one for Foster. He was obviously pleased at the outcome of the evening. I raised an eyebrow archly.

When Mr. and Mrs. John D. Rockefeller, Jr., came to Yaddo for dinner some months later, I regretted they had not been able to coordinate their visit with that of Mr. Washington's. The reputation of the senior John D. Rockefeller was mixed; one's personal assessment of him depended on whom was asked. The bright reporter Mrs. Ida Tarbell, in her incisive articles serialized in *McClure's* between 1902 and 1904, had exposed the evil practices of the Standard Oil Company: Rockefeller was a grasping monster of monopoly, an un-feeling and hard-nosed businessman. She had exposed the company's unfair practices and painted an ugly man. He had ruined capitalism by not playing by the rules of ethical business and he had destroyed his competition and ruined countless individuals while exhibiting an unemotional demeanor.

I permitted myself to look at the other side, his philanthropy. I personally knew he was a curiously pious Baptist, a generous philanthropist, and he held a special feeling for the Negro education cause, and in fact the cause of women. We had corresponded frequently, and I was eager to hear about his interests in educational causes of the South, especially since Foster, at his roots a Southern man and one who believed in the future of the South, had directed some philanthropy to institutions in Georgia and to Alabama. John D. Senior and Spencer had finance, railroads, the Union Club, the Metropolitan Museum in common. I was most interested in Senior's recent philanthropy, and in his funding of a school in Atlanta, Georgia, for the education of young Negro women.

As it turned out, it was Senior's son and his wife who dined with us at Yaddo, through the connection of Foster. Both were active on the General Education Board in New York, a philanthropic group whose mission was the promotion of education within the United States of America, "without distinction of race, sex or creed."[59] Through Foster, Southern institutions had reached out to the Board with their pleas for funds, and Foster had interested the senior Rockefeller. (Perhaps the plucky Mrs. Tarbell's investigative journalism had pricked his balloon: Senior's life lately was turning from business to philanthropy.[60]) Nevertheless, John D. Junior now carried forth Dad's business and Foster and I were looking to direct some funds towards our causes.

Mrs. Rockefeller, in cream gown and matching gloves, wore around her neck a dazzling triple strand of emeralds, and her hair was upswept in perfect Gibson-girl "do." She was effervescent and gay throughout the evening while the men discussed business. I strained to overhear the spirited conversations of the men and also to listen graciously as Mrs. R. expressed perhaps an undue appreciation of my book of poetry which Foster had kindly sent ahead of my invitation. I must confess she was quite talkative about subjects I had little interest in, and try as I may, I couldn't find the will or even the opportunity for interjection. I knew the Rockefellers were good friends of Foster's. I knew they had visited Abenia often and enjoyed the magical boat cruises on the *Pocahontas,* and so I was my most charming and indulgent. Hospitality at Yaddo was well-known, but with some dinner guests it was a labor of love... after which I chastised myself for my ungenerous heart.

There was one beautiful person whom I most regretted never having at out table at Yaddo, though her presence was with me often in my tower room when my eyes gave me great pain, and my mornings were dim and cloudy. She was the lovely Helen Keller.

My entire life I had fought arterial sclerosis which caused hemorrhages in my eyes and weakened the vision for a period of days, sometimes longer. Often I had to have complete rest and live "in the shadow" to protect my eyesight. My gnawing fear of blindness I kept at bay, for the most part, but I knew at any moment it might creep into my life as my worst enemy. In January of 1905 I suffered an eye hemorrhage on a house-party weekend at Watch Hill, the result of pressure on my eye artery from an irregular heart beat. I was sent home to live "in shadow" to prevent blindness, and then, Deliverance! The blood clot dissolved. Therefore when I met the spirited, highly intelligent Helen Keller in New York, her life and her approach to it intrigued me as no other human model had. We had a warm meeting at a conference in the city, and I was struck with her positive nature and extraordinary achievements. We also had in common certain political views which she so far had not felt compelled to make public. (We were at heart socialists.) When my eyesight failed me, as it did from time to time, I held her up as my model of perseverance. I enjoyed hearing from her, but I treasure in particular two letters to me, typewritten and signed in pencil with her printed block letters.

"*My dear lady, what you say is especially encouraging because you have proved it yourself. Despite darkness and suffering you have shown in a beautiful way how the inner being can conquer the outer being, and I who am happy feel your sunshine and love it. I thank you, too, for the plaque. In its light, graceful form and delicate tracery it is most gratifying to my touch.*"[61]

Some years later when the worst crisis of my eyes occurred, she sent me this letter of cheer and faith.

"*My heart goest out, full of grief and tenderness, to you in your great deprivation. I long to take your hand in mine and let you feel the living sympathy that no eye can see. But since this may not be, I send you this little message knowing that your brave spirit finds comfort in a light more*

*beautiful than the light of the sun... heart-light friendship
and kindness... I remember how you put my hand on your
face and I still have the dear image in my touch. Afterwards,
you made me very happy by sending a copy of* Christolan
*that I could read myself. It had been read to me before; when
I found it in raised letters, I felt that I possessed its beauty
and sweetness more completely. I hope you will be strong
soon, dear lady, and I pray that you may find great consola-
tion in the evidence of things unseen which has sustained
me so often when I have felt discouraged and isolated. My
teacher sends her sympathy and kindest remembrances.
Will you kindly lay your hand on this page, that you may
see my love-sign?*

    Your loving friend,
    H-e-l-e-n K-e-l-l-e-r [printed in pencil]."[62]

Her life and her example made pale the existence
of ladies and gentlemen I knew who complained and
whined about their worldly matters and their small
adversities, never realizing how blinded they were to
matters that count.

Because Foster, Spencer and I shared so many
friends, we could entertain them at either Abenia or at
Yaddo. At Yaddo we hosted dramatic readings and concerts, and held dinner conferences to further Spencer's
causes for the Red Cross, the Arts League in New York,
the Metropolitan Museum, the women's Teachers College he had founded at Columbia University, or for some
hospital cause. Between Abenia on Lake George and
Yaddo in Saratoga Springs, many a gathering was held

designed to promote interest and funds to further the cause of education, in New York as well as in the South.

Among our strong friendships was that with Bishop William Doane of the Albany Episcopal Diocese, who often was a guest at Yaddo. My views on religion were more ecumenical and non-denominational but Foster was a devotee of the liturgy and doctrine of the Episcopal Church and was the most widely known laymen in the circles of the Episcopal Church in America. Often Bishop Doane came to Yaddo and sat in the rose garden with Foster and me, discussing religious topics and church doctrine.[63]

In truth, I am a more non-traditional spiritual being and don't require a specific denomination of Christianity to channel my relationship to Jesus. I am a "spiritual linguist. I can talk to each one in his own language. I can be all things to all men."[64] I correspond with the Bishop of Syria, through a translator, and he (an Orthodox Christian) and I (with my "own religion") together commune in the same spirit without having the same religious denomination. How long we Christians let our "hair-splitting religious differences over the Quality of his divinity keep us from understanding the Reality of His Humanity: too long we have waged war over His immaculate birth and have forgotten, in the dispute, to consider fully his Immaculate Life. Too long we have emphasized the theological dogma of his Godhood, ignoring the supreme lesson of his Manhood: the lesson which shines forth as an effulgent truth the more we ponder it... that to EVERY man it is given to become a son of God."[65] And when man recognizes the

Humanity of Christ, he must see the Democracy of Christ, as well. He loved the Mighty, and the Lowly.[66] I so tire of people claiming Him for the rich or the poor, to suit their own goals. And using Bible verses to back up their positions.

Off I go again, Spencer will chide, on my religious tangents. I now am learning to check my tongue and frame my philosophical notions on paper. And reader, I *am* rewarded by the critics. The religious philosophy of Katrina Trask expressed through someone else, the *lesson* shown through image, metaphor, drama, character, but expressed, at least. Already I have offered my views on sin and forgiveness through *Night and Morning,* my creation of adulterous Miriam whom Christ forgives. And, yes, the world has liked it, and the reviewers complimented the lushness of my expression. The critical world was moved by Elizabeth Dearfield's pure love in my novel *Free Not Bound,* her clear religious view of the Greater truths surviving censure from narrow minded men and from exclusive religious denominations which preach love and show pride and condemnation. She left the judgment to God [67] and let her life reflect the ideals of Jesus. (Elizabeth is my favorite creation, my favorite persona.)

By the way, you should know that I no longer am publishing anonymously. *Under King Constantine,* printed with no attribution in 1892, has now been through three more editions here and my authorship is known. *"Look, Spencer,"* I had called out from my study one morning. *"I am evidently now in the category of Elizabeth Barrett Browning and George Elliot. Here, in the* Times, *they are heralding me as not just 'talented' but 'genius.' They say 'the great woman poet and dramatist has at last arrived.'*[68]

King Constantine is a great success. My writing career is reaching full stride now, and consumes my thoughts. The words lie on my pillow at night, the characters live at my breakfast table and walk beside me in the garden. I hear the rhythm of my poems in my sleep, and leap up to record the lines. I try to write four hours a day, in the tower room. I write verses rapidly, then revise and re-do. I am lost in my inner world of creating. I feel attuned to all rhythms around me; I own, now, a heightened sensitivity. Perhaps, at last, it is for this reason I was fashioned by the Creator: to reach my full Woman's potential, to love my fellow man and God, and TO WRITE.

In recent years I also choose to write without the guise of fictional characters who dramatize my views. I was so incensed by the Episcopal Convention in Boston and their official (and officious) decisions on divorce and church law, that I wrote an article for *The Arena* in early 1905. How could a church waste its time arguing over canons of exclusion? Why stress restrictions and punishments, instead of stressing self-discipline and self-development, which would obviate the need for divorce in the first place? Divorce was certainly a growing evil in our country, but I felt it should NOT be combatted by negative church divorce laws or church regulations. The church should teach with Light, not Legislation.

These religious views regarding the role and practices of the church were Spencer's as well as mine but they never lessened our love of the beautiful language of the Episcopal liturgy which we used each Sunday evening at vespers with our entire Yaddo household when we gathered as a family at the Stone Tower. (We had changed the not very efficient ice-house into a lovely chapel.) I designed and had printed lovely prayer books for all of the household members and visiting friends so that they could familiarize themselves with the verses and responses which we used. After Spencer led our congregation in the service, we enjoyed the walk back through the Queens Woods to Yaddo mansion for warming cider or cooling lemonade and refreshments. We also used Episcopal devotionals in the brief service we had with our household each morning at ten.

The Bishop of Albany was always one of our closest friends, and our particular liberal views about church law and dogma never came between our friendship and mutual devotion. We were keen supporters of Bethesda Episcopal Church in Saratoga and answered calls for help with respect to the organ, and donated the stained glass window depicting Christ's miracle at the Bethesda pool. Inwardly, we chose a "universal" religion which was positive, inclusive, humanistic, and devoted to the ideals set forth by Jesus Christ. We loved the beauty of the words of the Bible and the humanity of its stories. But most of all we loved Bishop Doane.

I began by sharing with you our wonderful cast of close friends who enriched our lives, and so I must tell you now about friends from business who joined this more personal sphere. One such example was a man who has impacted our world like no other, and with whom we have enjoyed over twenty-five years of friendship. That friend is Mr. Thomas Alva Edison, and of course his wife Mina. Many a happy vacation we shared with them up on Lake Champlain, or in the Adirondacks in the early days. Thomas Edison and Spencer began an association when the inventor and ingenious personality came looking for financial backing, mainly to financiers J. P. Morgan and Henry Villard, but also to Spencer Trask and Company.

The investors had decided to take a chance on Edison's incandescent light bulb and its practical application in the world: they had to put up the financing during the experimental period to make the bulb stay lit for more than a few hours. After the investors went to Menlo Park in New Jersey to watch the dramatic and successful demonstration, they backed the formation of the Edison Electric Light Company to manufacture electricity, receiving stock shares themselves. They founded a different company to distribute the power to light the bulbs and again the investors received substantial stock in this company. To be safe, electrical wires were buried, finally, under the streets of New York after the great disruptive Blizzard of 1888; it was an enormous task for workers digging through pavement and fighting piles of horse dung and garbage while enduring the doubting glances of New Yorkers.

The first generators for an electrical network were created at the Pearl Street Station. There were uncertain days but soon the city was transformed from gas light to electric light; Spencer Trask and Company glowed with electricity as did Morgan's Wall Street office. As new generating stations were required in Brooklyn and uptown in Manhattan, Spencer was named president of Edison Illuminating, and he moved the office into his own office building, where he served the board for five years. He passed the reins to Foster during the awful year we lost our fourth baby and went off to Europe. Later on when the company was reorganized into General Electric, Spencer would serve on that board.[69]

Spencer's firm also supported Edison in another enterprise, that of the phonograph, which Thomas saw not as useful for entertainment, but for the keeping of business and historical records. We were among the first to hear the recording of Tennyson reading his *Charge of the Light Brigade,* in deep and powerful tones, which brought tears to my eyes. (My Junius had loved that poem as read by his father.) Back in 1898 we were delighted to receive from Thomas the gift of a phonograph for our home in Brooklyn. By 1907 the North American Phonograph Company had sold nearly twenty million records[70] and we soon would have a phonograph in all our homes, from the apartment in New York, to Tuxedo Park, to Yaddo.

Thomas and I shared many a conversation and similar views on violence and war; he refused during World War I to work on any weapons when the government enlisted his inventiveness in the service of the United States. I knew his distrust of "financial men," his preference for singular and tangible work in a laboratory, but he admired Spencer as a rare financier without greed, a man to be trusted.

Adolph Ochs, our Tennessee friend who publishes the *New York Times*, came into our lives when Spencer sought to rescue the floundering paper in the city and was approached by the confident, aggressive, and refreshingly ethical publisher from Chattanooga. He was persuasive enough for Spencer, and the rest is well known. Spencer and several associates underwrote and re-organized the paper and placed Adolph at the helm as publisher. The *Times* would record for its readers the crazy gyrations of our time without partiality: wild prosperity and then busts and panics; corruption and acts of philanthropy; conflicting views over the gold standard; open free enterprise versus curbs on monopolies; isolationism versus protectionism; Democrats versus Republicans.[71]

Adolph vowed to keep the news impartial, and sometimes he and Spencer disagreed on issues, and emphasis, and inclusion, but the paper became financially sound and worth the investment. Adolph proudly turned down Tammany Hall offers for large blocks of subscriptions lest he appear "on the take" and he turned down advertisers whose products he found unethical or unsubstantiated. Spencer was aghast when Adolph lowered the price of the paper from three cents to one cent during a particularly bad time. Adolph believed readers bought the scandalous and inflaming "yellow sheets" of the competing newspapers because they were cheaper. He said readers would prefer spending the same money on a good and impartial newspaper of integrity. And he was right. Because of Adolph's fine character, shrewd insight, and good business methods the paper became respected and revered and financially successful.

Adolph and Spencer on the whole maintained a good relationship and he and Effie became friends of ours, often coming to Yaddo. Foster writes his balanced and revered editorials for the paper and I too send articles or letters or poems which find their way into print there. I always ask for no special consideration but of course I know there is "pressure" to allow my work or views at least to be printed without editorial judgment. In the *Book Review* section of the *Times*, I ask for no "good reviews" when they are not merited.

Other special friends of the Trasks included established artists in the city — sculptors, painters and photographers — especially Eastman Johnson, Augustus Saint-Gaudens, Ordway Partridge, Penn Browning and all our friends at the National Arts Club which Spencer, along with Mr. Frick, had established in the city. (I am proud of my husband who insisted that women be allowed to join from the beginning).[72] We attended soirees and afternoon teas in various ateliers in New York in the early days of our marriage and kept ourselves in the vanguard of artistic developments and expressions. Spencer loved the world of art, and I think it sad that he was not gifted a talent for painting or sculpture himself in order to express the creativity he so naturally owned. But he created beauty in our estate, and pageantry in our lives, and I am ever grateful to be given a role on his stage.

I must include among our "special friends who mattered" our own slight, soft-spoken attorney Edward

Morse Shepard who is a great associate of my husband's and a devoted friend to me. We had known him in the old days in Brooklyn. Edward and Foster were among those who formed the Young Man's Democratic Party and, as idealistic young lads, pushed for Civil Service reform. Later in their lives, Foster now armed with substantial wealth, they shared philanthropy in their common support of Hampton Institute in Virginia, the school set up after the Civil War to instruct Negroes in agricultural, industrial, and mechanical arts.[73]

Edward was also a neighbor of Foster's on Lake George, had built his mansion Erlowest nearby on the west shore. There, he too staged lavish house-parties where political views were shared and campaign strategies hatched. Foster's dynamic personality often overshadowed that of his friend, and I frequently gazed with wonder at Foster Peabody as he stepped back to let a less dynamic man shine on many an occasion. That was so like Foster. And Foster often quipped that neither he nor Edward would ever marry because they could never marry me.

"Do you know how I described your true nature to the Governor last month, dear one?" I wanted Foster to know just how much I admired him, loved him.

"Do you realize the esteem I have for you, Foster? Here's what I say when one mentions George Foster Peabody: 'Smaller men cannot understand him: he lives in a strata where the atmosphere is too rare for them to breathe; but men of insight and of power appreciate him. He walks the earth the friend of man, the friend of God, serene, poised, undismayed and unafraid.' How does

THAT sound, my dear?"[74]

And Foster took my hand to his lips. He cherished my admiration, basked in my praise of him. In turn, my vanity was elevated through effusive letters from him, letters scribbled out on crested parchment notes from Abenia on the day following a dinner, or a presentation, or a gathering where we might have been together.

"How splendidly beautiful you were tonight, how more the delicious in your every move. How splendidly queenly! My most humble and knightly recognition to you most rare Lady for all the splendid inspiration and help. Fare thee well my love. Faithfully yours only and always, Foster."[75]

My husband loved me with all his heart, but Foster too placed me center stage in his life and watched with adoration his favorite actress play the role of Queen. I was devoted to my steadfast husband Spencer, I loved him, and at the same time I fell in love with Foster's passionate words and the soft, vulnerable, sentimental side of him. The three of us together created something greater than the parts. Each part would suffer immeasurably were there the loss of the whole.

Foster himself had planted the seed for my next real estate adventure. It started with my chest pains, and the return of hemorrhages in my eye. The menacing shadow in my life was the arterial sclerosis. There were times when I endured months of bed rest, and then

I had longer periods of impunity from pain. Sometimes the eye problems required living in low light, curtains drawn. When my first born was but a babe I had been forced to leave him with my mother and live abroad for many long months, taking the water cures. As of late, I had acquired the skill of pushing my health problems behind me, like Satan, and refused to consider that my vision would be taken from me when I depended on it so direly for my writing. But in 1905 the pains came back more frequently now, followed by more periods of weakened vision.

"You look so tired, Katrina. I do believe your life's pace in Saratoga is destroying you. Too many dinners, too many concerts at Yaddo, too many meetings of this and that. Too much writing and corresponding with too many people. Come to the lake, my dear. I know you will regain your color and your strength. Your heart needs rest."

Foster had known I was feeling weak, and he and Spencer were continually seeking medical advice and discussing remedies which might improve my condition. The heart issues would not go away, but I was determined not to go back to Europe for more treatments. Surely Nature could heal me. One night at Yaddo I was suddenly awakened with an ominous feeling. I was filled with a stirring in my whole being. I felt a presence in my room, entreating me to, to do what? What WAS it, this energy circulating at my bedside?

"What will you have me do?" I whispered.

"Where shall I go?"

"To the lake. To the lake."[76]

A prophecy for me, a spirit directing my will.

Often I have felt this special power in my life. I have felt connected to something other-worldly. I admit, only *half* jokingly, that I believe in a fairy-world. There had been other clear directive visions, which I have previously described in my *Chronicles*, especially the vision of our Pine Garde artists' colony which led us to our grand plan for Yaddo's future. My visions always have proven constructive and they have moved me forward on my life's path.

The prophecy must refer to Lake George. The place I had cherished on summer vacations as a very young girl. My secret afternoon place, straw hat, Browning and Tennyson, in the boat, gently jostled by the waves slapping in and withdrawing. I remembered the rhythmic hypnotic force of those waves washing against the moored boat, and the curtain of contentment which drew around me. Afternoon dozing on Lake George. Amidst the rhythm and pictures of *My Last Duchess* and the wistful man of Locksley Hall. I remembered that magical summer when Papa had brought us to Lake George for two months when I was thirteen, existing on the fragile line between childhood and womanhood. There on the lake I had experienced a quickening of body and of emotions. The exquisite rapture of being one with nature filled my mind with wonder about God and his universe, and it also kindled questions about Love. Who would be the Prince Charming in my life? I wanted to be *ready* intellectually for that Prince, I wanted to study more, learn more, and reach my potential before *my* special days of Love.

"*All the external beauty of life, which so stirred me,*

seemed in a curious way, a symbol. I did not understand, not in the least, but I was conscious that it was vastly significant and symbolical. I had a curious prescience that everything in Nature would one day hold meaning for me."[77] That summer of 1866 on Lake George was significant in another way, too. I began to reason, to think, to formulate my own theories of religion, of politics, of the church, and I knew I was veering out bravely from accepted views. But reader, you must know that I also was a merry and care-free girl in those days, too, and loved walking with Papa's older friend past the big hotel to watch the adult women in their silks dancing and being so beautiful and captivating. And I loved the picnics to Diamond Island, so rife with rich history which filled my imagination. Often I rowed out alone to this island, its north end like the prow of a ship, and I would wander about the pine forest, or sit on the rocks, imagining the days of the French and Indian War, seeing a quick flash of war-paint and feathers just behind the tree.

Lake George. It was pre-ordained that I should return. Spencer would take me to the lake. We would rent a place, on an island. Yes, an island, perhaps near our friends Edward Shepard at Erlowest and Foster at Abenia. Lake George. A beautiful and healing retreat. Next summer. ❧

George Foster Peabody, Katrina Trask, and
the artist Eastman Johnson, about 1890.
{ Courtesy Saratoga Springs History Museum }

Chapter Four

Lady of the Lake

Island living on Lake George was a romantic adventure in the beginning. A hopeful summer of change and relaxation to escape the social rounds in Saratoga and to renew my fading health, we told friends. We secretly loved the Bohemian spirit of "trying on" the unusual, and so in the early spring Spencer rented Clay Island for our experiment in summer living. It was also called Belvoir Island, and we chose this second name because Spencer and I liked the sound of it and because it did afford "beautiful views." It had some scattered cottages, one good-size house, and enough property to set up a number of tents for living the true outdoor life close to Nature.

We brought with us for the summer James, Arthur, Betty, Bridget and Shannon from the Yaddo household because they had been with us the longest and they particularly loved the out-of-doors. Most of the other Yaddo professionals needed for our experiment would stay in the house and cottages at the north end of the island while we "tented." I'd read numerous articles on the benefits of fresh air, and here we would sleep in such a setting. Spencer and I thought it so gay and refreshing and healthful.

Bridget and Arthur along with a Yaddo farm crew came up ahead of us in late June. The men were to set up the ten waterproof tents on platforms steadied by guy wires and poles (they formed an unusual cream-colored village), and especially prepare the largest one for us, following explicit directions to render it comfortable and hospitable.

I had made a list of my own needs to arrive at "comfortable" in my fabric home: enough space for a writing desk and a commodious brass bed; some wicker chairs arranged attractively; a table or two for vases of roses; a linen chest for my good personal linens from Madeira; storage space for my books; and tables for the various newspapers which Arthur would fetch for us daily from the mainland. A day bed or chaise lounge was important, I added: quite often I had to be "in horizontal" when I was writing or reading.

I sent up five small Turkish prayer rugs and the new Sarouk with floral sprays on a wine red field. Softness and beauty for under our feet, instead of the hard wood platform. Spencer and I liked the riot of color in the rugs, the strong reds and blues, rugs laid over each other to make our tent-room plush and aesthetically pleasing. We would not be completely rustic here. Oh, and the lovely Oriental fans for "wall" decoration, as well as our Chinese lanterns which I wanted strung about the tent community for night ambience. My list was getting longer.

Betty was in charge of the good linens and silverware for dining. Silver should sparkle regardless of its environment. There was a special tent for the laundry with an intricate many-armed European drying rack and large tables for Betty's expert ironing. I brought my own embroidered coverlets and bed clothes, a host of white day gowns which were now my dress *d'habitude*, plus boxes of potpourri and powder, hair pins and combs, and my favorite silver-mounted bristle brush, monogrammed, from the dresser set Spencer had given me as a wedding gift. Sentimental, I know, but my treasures bring me great joy.

To keep myself occupied I brought numerous older newspaper clippings from our New York press service which I had put aside for organizing in a scrapbook and, of course, my writing materials, including calligraphy pens. "I do *understand, my darling,*" had said Spencer, "*that you need some objects from home if you are to feel happy here and regain your strength. Our home 'away' should be a reflection of us,*" he said, "*and it should have all the comforts on which we have come to rely.*"

Spencer was particularly pleased because our tents had "windows," opaque squares mimicking true windows, as well as openings in the wall which we covered with gauze to welcome fresh lake air and sunlight, but discourage insects.[78] He had chosen from the brochures the tents which came with scallops and brightly striped awnings — they were very stylish — as a further protection from inclement weather which could descend on us unexpectedly, as we were to discover. Spencer, true to his nature, stayed interminably busy in our new location. His launch would take him each day to the mainland for "business" and mail, then back to Belvoir.

During the time he was "on island" he was often experimenting with day-to-day practicalities: new methods for waste disposal in our tent community; overseeing the progress in our vegetable garden and berry patch; or poring over his brochures on generators and boats.

Before our mid-summer arrival, one of our newest agricultural professionals had been sent ahead to start the gardens. He was also new to America and to our Northeast area, and sent a message down to Yaddo announcing that we may not be at all comfortable on the lake. It was the mosquitoes, he had said. Horrible biting small flies that clustered about your neck and hairline and left swollen eyes and itching skin which made sleep impossible. Not just ordinary mosquitoes, he had emphasized. Then he reported back that they had gone, towards the end of June. "Of course, it's the black flies," said another man in the farm household — the famous *Adirondack* black flies. They live in the area from mid-May to mid-June, and no one works in the garden turning over the soil without protective netting or ointment during that period. And without wearing dark clothes. I suppose that, by not actually spading at Yaddo, only enjoying my garden as it came into bloom, I was blithely unaware of the black-fly matter. Perhaps the flies prospered only in the lake environment or the mountains up north.

All was perfect when we arrived in early July. The days were warm. The usual cold, clear lake had lost its frozen winter chill, and the morning skies began a shy melon-colored line over the blackness of the mountain range, then erupted bright pink as the sun burst forth on our early-rising days. And evenings were magical. We were pleased with our touch of the Oriental in strings of Chinese lanterns stretched about the tents and trees, their candle-lit bright orange shapes dramatic against a night sky. (Later, on our other island, we would add a generator for electric lights.)

Sometimes after a languid sunset and the sudden collapse into night Spencer and I sat on a big rock at water's edge and we felt we could easily be in a Far Eastern kingdom. We were lost in time under a canopy of brilliant stars overhead, alone on our rock, looking back into our village of tents outlined by the orange paper lanterns. The night peepers began their music, then the bass of the frogs entered the composition, and then over the water came the plaintive oboe notes of the loons (always in pairs and mated for life) thrillingly close to the two of us on the rock. The night concert evoked the perfect plan of Nature. I tell you, reader, the Trasks were living a dream in our new island paradise.

Our Belvoir Island was off shore from the charming hamlet of Bolton Landing, a stop for the tourist steam boats on the western shore. From our property one could see to the north the two-year-old luxury Hotel Sagamore on Green Island, just over the bridgeway from town. Mr. John Boulton Simpson, a business friend of Spencer's from New York city, had with four other investors bought Green Island and built the grand hotel which was already drawing an international clientele. Commodore Simpson owned the impressive 80-foot yacht *Fanita* which steamed up and down the lake, sometimes hosting state senators and the Forest

Commissioner to lobby for Lake George issues, sometimes bringing party-goers to his famous "chowder parties" held *en plein air* at some striking spot on the water. Spencer had many a conversation with him that summer regarding the possible creation of a yacht club on Lake George; they were members of the same men's clubs and arts boards in the city and had much in common.

Farther north and on the east side was Shelving Rock Mountain where, high up on its side, George Owen Knapp was building a grand estate to command sweeping views up and down the lake. From a boat one could see hundreds of laborers up on the ledge working like bees digging out carriage paths, building the house foundations, laying tracks for a funicular rail car from the base of the mountain directly into the basement of the house on top. Mr. Knapp was a co-founder of Union Carbide Company and was acquiring more and more acreage around the lake, especially near Paradise Bay. (He was another friend of Spencer's who had expressed interest in creating a private club on the lake.)

To the northwest was Tongue Mountain, sanctuary to wild birds, animals, and rattlesnakes. The mountain jutted like a tongue into the lake to form lovely, protected Northwest Bay. Sailboats and motorized yachts regularly passed between Belvoir Island and tiny Recluse Island, a stone's throw from us. They steered deftly past hidden rocks and shoals on their way north to the Sagamore, or perhaps to the even-wilder northern part of the lake. Early on a summer day boaters headed north past our rented cottages and tents, full of expectations to drop anchor in Paradise or one of the other protected bays, with their house guests and elaborate picnics; or to motor leisurely among the islands of the Narrows, peopled by outcrops of jagged rocks, sentinel pines, and possessive sea gulls; or to venture further north to the end of the lake which still resembled the pristine time of Fenimore Cooper's Mohicans.

Many well-traveled friends and even foreigners have noted they knew of no other place, except Lake Como, more beautiful than this lake; and Lake Como they found superior because of the stunning architecture along the shores. I wrote in my diary that Lake George may lack "a certain picturesqueness and historic charm, but instead leaves a virgin loveliness that adds to its charm."[79] I found its deserted and rugged wilderness setting the perfect place to rest and reflect, and perhaps resume my writing career when I felt stronger.

Spencer was more a social animal than I, and already he had conferred with Foster and his brothers Charles and Royal about constructing a clubhouse somewhere on the shore and creating a yacht club for socializing on the lake. They had been joined by other dynamic and financially-sound lake neighbors like Mr. Bixby, Mr. Simpson, Mr. Knapp, who envisioned a refined club where people of similar taste and background could enjoy boating, tennis, golf, billiards, and "wholesome games and sports."[80] They informally had begun to look at various locations which would provide a protected harbor for boating and enough property for a nine-hole golf course. While they and their friends explored real estate and began the process of gathering suitable backers for such a club, I read and relaxed.

I luxuriated in the quiet of my island home, enjoying morning hours, resting in the afternoons, doing some correspondence. My imagination was freed in the quiet beauty of the changing landscapes of the lake, and I began to drift into scenarios of a *permanent* summer place for the Trasks here on Lake George. I noticed that Spencer had already allowed himself that possibility as he was exploring ideas for a club.

Foster quite often arrived at Belvoir with great ceremony in late afternoon, his prized roses intertwined among the boat's pillars, hand held in salute as I met him at our dock. The *Pocahontas* always brought refreshment on its deck: monogrammed silver trays were often laden with plates of cheese straws and tomato sandwiches and cut-glass pitchers of lemonade. The boat was rigged formally with a table outfitted in damask linens holding the food trays and miniature vases of "Katrina pink" roses.

Foster had a flair for drama, Spencer used to say, but then Spencer had married me, and he was accustomed to my own grand entrances and exits. Furthermore, Spencer himself enjoyed costume and elaborate sets more than anyone. At Yaddo we all knew Spencer could create an extravagant theatrical event down to the last written cue. Pageantry could be staged anywhere, and here on this sparkling lake it was irresistible.

When I felt stronger we motored about the lake. The *Pocahontas*, nearly fifty-five feet long, could carry seventy-five guests; its wicker seats set in rows on the deck could also be removed and placed on an island camp-site for a day of fishing, and perhaps dinner by the fire. More frequently it was just we three friends (and often Allena, too) cruising about, nosing in and out of bays along the west shore looking at some of the newer estates rising on the rocks around Bolton Landing, expressing our opinions of their style and sharing recent news of their unique residents.

Mostly we motored south toward the village of Caldwell (later re-named Lake George, as no-one thought of the town by any other name). We passed Rockledge, owned by the Tuttles, where composer Sidney Homer and his wife Louise were renting for the summer. I had long been a fan of Louise Homer, the internationally-acclaimed star of the Metropolitan Opera, and Spencer and I had acquired the Victor Talking Machine recording of hers, the first successful recording of a voice.[81] It was our favorite on the new phonograph from Mr. Edison. I longed to try to make social contact with this prima-donna contralto because Mrs. Homer was a woman I admired greatly, one who effortlessly combined professional career with a loving family and who dauntlessly overcame personal set-backs. When Louise was not on tour a year ago, I had been too ill to receive them at Yaddo.

Our neighbor to the north in Bolton Landing, W. K. Bixby, told us the Homers were planning to buy land from him to build their summer house farther up on the lake near his property. He thought they would be "a cultural ornament" for the area.[82] Mr. Bixby, a self-made industrialist, philanthropist, and collector from St. Louis, had come to his wife's native Bolton Landing and had built his Greek Revival mansion on Mohican Point in 1902. An avid reader (he was devoted to Keats), collector, sportsman, and world traveler, Mr. Bixby also was the largest landowner in the area.

Heading south to Caldwell we enjoyed the familiar view of Foster's Abenia, and Edward Shepard's Erlowest on our starboard, this latter a granite mansion with a distinctive silhouette high on the cliff, framed by spectacular specimen trees and a sweeping lawn. Brooklyn friends since their early twenties, both now well-to-do gentlemen, Foster and Edward shared common interests: the Episcopal Church, art, gardening, conservation of natural resources, politics. In that order. Foster was always promoting Edward for political offices, but Foster seemed to have more enthusiasm for him than the voters.[83] They were traveling companions, as well, and had some nice European tours which inspired their tastes.

More often on the lake we headed east, away from man's footprint and his grand dwellings, seeking the perfect stillness of Paradise Bay. We would silence the motor and sit there reverently with the sun's rays low on our backs, and we felt as though we had been chosen, blessed among man and woman, to be at this place, God's own stage.

I had come to the lake for recuperation, but long before this an idea had been budding within me, a dream I had sequestered for some time, since we began visiting Foster and Edward. The Trasks should have a permanent summer place on an island in Lake George, less formal than Yaddo (and less social than Abenia!).

Not a *big* island like Belvoir, but a more manageable setting for a month or two of summer. By the end of our rental period that year, I felt I had discovered just the place. One just had to use a little imagination and ingenuity to make it happen. And of course, one had to convince Spencer.

Before I go any further, however, it is important to pause and tell you that Lake George was not only for us, those who were well-to-do and blessed in our circumstances. It was also a lake for others, the less fortunate. I'll tell you of an earlier plan — a very separate dream — I had involving Lake George, and how it came to fruition just a few years ago. Actually, there were *two* plans, and they came together in a marvelous way. They were born of my interest in the arts, my belief in the restorative power of Nature, and the ever-present concern for those less privileged than the Trasks — and they involved a family friend not yet introduced. My feelings on certain social issues were more and more informing my actions.

When they were still with us, my young Junius and his older sister had astonished me continually with their keen insight and their inborn compassion. In my heart was "the Junius question," spoken by my sweet boy as our carriage one day had hurried through a tenement section of Manhattan: "Why should God give Junius such a pretty house, and that poor boy such a nasty house?" It was a social question which I often asked, and one I wrestled with in my conscience. Looking at the vast disparity in wealth between social classes here in America at the beginning of the twentieth century, I thought of dire consequences: revolt, uprisings, violent overthrowing of the social order. I wrote in my diary one day:

"The wretched inequality of life staggers me. What right have I to an income that enables me to live a life of ease and luxury whilst my fellow man can wrest by their toil only the merest pittance. It is all wrong. The time will come when the distribution of wealth will be very different.... in the meantime, however, no one alone can change the established order: we can only go on working and doing our best to make new laws and to help on a new spiritual order."[84]

The disparity in wealth and opportunity troubled me, and I felt it was only a matter of time before countries with such social disparities would shudder with revolution. In our country there had been some terrible labor strikes, with ghastly endings. I was a *social* socialist and I felt that those to whom much had been given, in return, *owed* something back to their world. I was not in my heart an *economic* socialist, for they undermined the system which produced the wealth. To avoid social revolution, I had come to believe that educated, enlightened, and wealthy individuals must take the lead in creating a spiritual order. Those individuals who COULD, in fact *SHOULD* care for those who "lived without the light" and suffered in the under-class of America.

The encouraging news to me was that philanthropy in New York city was surprisingly widespread among the Gilded Age titans of industry, and also among some wives. Not to say that the society mavens eschewed the extravagant dinners and the society balls and the appointments with dressmakers. Most traditional "society" women I have found to be ultimately frivolous. But many *did* reach out, strongly determined to soar above restriction, tradition, bigotry. Of course, the eleemosynary work had to be *subtle* and kept "under the wire" of acceptability, not appearing as "blatant socialism." The very word made many shudder. It seemed to me that in the field of Gilded Age philanthropy, for the most part, the men supported the area of higher education, the libraries, the funding of brick-and-mortar institutions, while the women promoted social change in housing, the work place, and in advancements for immigrants, women, children, and Negroes.

Working in the reform field for better conditions for women and children were a few feisty society women from both the old- and new-moneyed "New York 400" (those who would fit in Mrs. Astor's ballroom). These women seemed to feel the tension which I often felt, the propriety and restrictions of their upbringing and at the same time the urge to be more active and modern in the world. They joined, at least in *spirit,* some working class reformers like the Emma Goldberg- and Rose Pastor-type women who presented to the majority of Americans as brash and coarse. These quite disparate classes of reform-minded women did find it hard to be together socially in a room, even if they worked for the same goals.

The exception, I think, was the blue-blood (Manhattan real-estate) Stokes family who stood by their pedigreed but reformist son Graham when he announced he would marry the Jewish socialist Red Rose Pastor in 1905.[85] I had smiled to visualize the family closing ranks and supporting "socialist policies" in their children and marriage outside their social class. They proceeded with stiff upper lip and faint praise. Their other son architect Isaac Newton Stokes, also reared in their 100-room summer "cottage" in the Berkshires, had stepped outside tradition like his brother and chosen to work in urban planning, building model tenement apartments in the city. His wife, the famous Edith Minturn Stokes, sculpted by Daniel Chester French and painted by John Singer Sargent, herself nurtured a progressive spirit and was a suffragette.

Because of my compromised health I could not be so physically active in the wider world as the Stokeses and others, and so I had to find my own causes closer to home in order to satisfy my charitable instincts. Therefore it was with *special* interest that I supported a woman with a great idea who lived *closer* to Lake George and Saratoga and was acting locally on a wider national problem. This woman was actually a family friend, a girl whom Spencer and I had watch grow into a lovely and caring young woman. She was Mary Wiltsie Fuller, from a substantial Troy family, and she had wrestled with the same questions we had, over the privileged in society and the less-fortunate.

Mary Fuller's question was quite specific: Why should not those whose financial circumstances denied them the rest and renewal of a summer vacation be given reasonable opportunity and access to Lake George? She was distressed by the horrid working conditions of women in the shirt and collar factories of Troy, New York, and had been working through the Episcopal societies to find a suitable place on Lake George to offer inexpensive vacations for these women and their children. She had seen the inside of steamy work-places, windows shut tight to protect the manufacturing process, the product valued over the *maker* of the product. These were young immigrant women, toiling in the "city of women," making Troy into the "Collar City" of the country.

Spencer, Foster, and I shared this concern and had begun our own search for such a property a few years ago. At the time, we had *two* thoughts in mind, one being to provide a place on Lake George for visiting women artists from the New York Arts Club (and, occasionally, men) who deserved peace and time away from the city. We purchased an older, modest camp (the "Stockwell Cottage") on the east side of the lake to use as an artists' retreat, which we named Amitola, after a young Indian chief who painted rainbows on the clouds. We later did some remodeling and asked the architect Stanford White to design a chalet-style lodge with Gothic touches for the site and we renamed the artists' complex Wakonda. Some years later, we were in luck in finding a second property when a hotel burned on the eastern shore of the lake at Crosbyside, not too far from Caldwell — and next to Amitola! Spencer and Foster purchased the damaged buildings and 150 acres, then they turned it over to me to refurbish. With the help of friends in Saratoga, Albany, and Troy — including Mary Fuller, of course — I oversaw repairs, and assembled some quite nice rugs and furnishings and made the larger Victorian house and some smaller cottages on the property look welcoming to the first group of working women we would invite.

With the two properties side by side, and each with a mission to offer rest and inspiration and renewal to young women, we ultimately joined them to form a vacation retreat for both artists *and* working women and called it the Wiawaka Holiday House. It would not be free, but it would be a very low-cost vacation retreat for a worthy clientele. The first summer season began on the fourth of July in 1903 when 172 women came up from Troy on the train to stay for the week at a modest cost of $3.50. Seeing the success of the endeavor, I soon decided to sell Wiawaka to Mary Fuller for $1.00 and a bouquet of native wildflowers.

Wiawaka came from the Abanake Indian term "the great spirit of God in women." I designed a brochure advertising the beauties of the location and the possibilities for recreation: canoeing, boating, lake bathing, croquet, hiking.[86] Soon women and their children, and some widows, were taking advantage of the extremely low rates. And they were being exposed to art from the artists staying at Wakonda. The whole project allowed me to express my views on the power, the Woman Spirit, which lies within all women, waiting for development, enrichment, if women would but seek it. Words of encouragement, a goal set... (education, practical training for a profession, spiritual study)… a life's purpose for these women. This I desired for them. I set about designing a handsome plaque for the wall of the Fuller House, a triptych whose words would serve to encourage the Woman Spirit in the Wiawaka women and to imbue the project with purpose.

For me, this act of charity allowed me in good conscience to live my exceptional life. And Wiawaka allowed me to be a "benevolent mother" to some of the guests' young children visiting on the lake, through small gifts and books and provisions for recreation there. I remembered how Christina loved her books, how her young imagination stretched with knowledge of history and literature and how she loved to create her own verses and plays. How she empathized with Homer's heroes and heroines, Shakespeare's ladies, tales from the Medieval period. I remembered how my insightful young ten-year-old read of Queen Victoria and wondered why she wasn't a "better queen who thought more of her humble subjects."[87] The Queen had recently had her Diamond Jubilee, but it celebrated only the throne.

"To think," she said, *"Queen Victoria had an opportunity to be a heroine, and failed to use it. Queen Victoria might have her name handed down through the ages as heroine, instead of being an ordinary old woman."*[88]

Christina had drawn up a plan for the English queen: she should go to Ireland and live among the people to see what their needs were. Such was a girl's view of social responsibility… and queens.

The little Wiawaka visitors were girls whose tired mothers came home from the factories at day's end with little inclination or ability to stir childhood wonder and imagination through reading and study. These women and their children were denied the healing power and the inspiration of a rural setting, the peacefulness of Nature. 1 had amassed some books to be kept at Wiawaka, and I so hoped to be able to go myself and be a nurturing force there by the lakeside... as soon as my strength returned.

I thought of Christina. *A little child shall lead them.*

It took almost five years to make Wiawaka a reality, but it was an important project in my life and influenced, I am certain, that fateful vision I had in the night, which beckoned me "to the lake, to the lake." Spending those glorious summer days on Belvoir Island in 1906 sealed my thoughts on the *other dream* of owning my own island on Lake George. By the end of the summer I finally found it: the most romantic and dramatic site I had seen on the Lake, not far from Bolton Landing off Homer Point. Three little islands, not one: the site would be the perfect place for *our* dream of Lake George, for *our* rest, inspiration, renewal. Three Brother Island it was called. I sailed past it, was captivated, and in my heart had already renamed it Triuna, three in one. Three islands. Three good friends: Spencer, Katrina, Foster. The triune nature of man and woman: body, mind, spirit. Having decided on the perfect location for our dream place on Lake George I was not to be deterred. But I tell you there was much lobbying against the idea.

Spencer: *"A romantic concept, my darling, but we must be practical."*

Foster: *"Must you tax your health with a site so formidable?"*

Ed Shepard: *"There is some low ground on the largest of the three which might not support bridges. And the distance to bring electricity?"*[89] *And what if you should need medical help quickly?*

But Spencer, Foster, and I did "pole" around the three islands ourselves, imagining how it could all happen. The initial exploration was a concession to me, and was meant to put the whole scheme to rest, but the opposite happened. The project became my "grand passion." Ed Shepard agreed that at Three Brother I would be farther away from "the annoyance of people," but he felt the better investment would be the Canoe Islands.

"We shall build our own Venice," I told Spencer. But this time he was stern-faced. The project was impossible. It was final, he said. I persisted. It was an insurmountable technological feat he said. Put your mind to it, dear, I told him. And then (I had known all along) Spencer decided to make the dream happen. He bought Three Brother Island from Helen Meyers for $2,500, three virgin islands off shore from Fish Point near Bolton Landing; and he bought from W. K. Bixby 200 feet of shore line for $812.50 to use as our base for boat transportation from the mainland.[90]

"We will build on virgin land, where no man has laid his hand, and we will show there is room for much more than an egg-shell. We will create the atmosphere and it will

abide," I wrote in my diary.[91]

"*The north island will be for the service part of the ménage and the welcoming entrance with little Gothic arch and belfry will set it off from the rest of the property. Beyond the archway we shall have a long vista and promenade under two colonnaded bridges, and above, sleeping apartments for our household and our guests. The south island we will keep for our own use. We will stain a wood brown the Norman-Gothic structures and the bridges; a soft chiming bell in the belfry will welcome in advance our guests as they approach. Medieval banners will mark each guest tent: the pine for Spencer, the rose for me, and for Allena, a four-leaf clover."* [92]

Later on, Bishop Doane in Albany would write a poem to engrave on our welcoming bell:
Sprinkle with holy sound the air,
O Blessed Bell.
Ring out all care.
Ring in True Love and Peace and Rest
To this triune Island of the blest.[93]

Spencer thought my architectural plan for the colonnaded bridges might be too "top-heavy," but I called on his memory of Firenze and the Bridge of Sighs. Was that structure, built in the most classic of Italian towns, too top-heavy? You, my dear, should concentrate on making a foundation, I told him. And, in his inimitable fashion, Spencer lined the pockets of the neighbors with more than ample payment for load after load of stones which were hauled over ice during the winter of 1906-

07, and left in perfect place around and between each island on our Triuna.[94] When spring thaw arrived, the stones dropped as planned to form the foundation for our Lake George Venice.

Many months earlier, when I first contemplated renting at Belvoir, I had in my heart selected Stanford White as the architect for a rustic summer place, should we find life on the lake agreeable. Spencer was a great admirer of White, and we had both liked his lodge design for our first experiment in artist retreats, Amitola.

Stanford White had spent time in Paris with Spencer's good friend the American sculptor Saint-Gaudens while he was chiseling his commissioned master work *David Glasgow Farragut*, the civil war Admiral and hero. (The bronze statue over eight feet tall and weighing over 900 pounds had been shipped to Madison Square Park in New York, and placed on a pedestal which White had designed in collaboration.[95]) In fact White and Saint-Gaudens had traveled together in France and Italy where White had taken inspiration from classic architecture: from the twelfth-century Church of Saint-Gilles in France came White's design ideas for a porch at St. Bartholomew's Church in New York.[96]

It was natural, then, that in dreaming of my own unique house on Lake George my thoughts had gone towards Stanford White. Famed architect Richard Morris Hunt was dead, and the wealthy clients, public and private, now looked to McKim, Mead and White as the foremost architectural firm in the country. Spencer saw him in New York frequently through his various arts societies and clubs. I always had admired Stanford

White's artistic eye for ornamental detail and decoration, as well his choice of fine building materials, and he was versatile. He had designed public buildings, banks, hotels, commemorative arches promoting civic pride and patriotism, lavish country homes in Long Island, Rhode Island, and along the Hudson, and expansive city mansions for the newly wealthy titans of industry, finance, transportation. He designed formal ornate villas, and also cozy, domestic family houses; he could dictate the design, and spend easily his client's money, often furnishing and decorating the homes with art treasures he personally had bought on trips to Europe and stored in warehouses in New York.[97]

But I also knew from friends and from reading outside reports that he could listen to the wishes of his oft-eccentric clients. Stanny White, Spencer often said, was "a gigantic personality" and a superb architect. Though I had never *socialized* with him, I knew he was a knowledgeable patron of the arts; certainly he was a congenial guest among the wealthy society patrons of the Northeast. We had friends who had seen Frederick Vanderbilt's newest and largest mansion going up on the Hudson River shore near the Mills mansion in Staatsburg; it was being lavishly furnished by Stanny. One could hardly read of great country houses and magnificent city monuments without the connection to White.

My house plans would never be as grand and extravagant and formal as these mansions. I wanted simplicity, but with artistic integrity and inward purpose. Truth be known, primarily I was attracted to the proposition of working with such an artistic, creative personality. I most certainly did not approve of White's personal life: his debauchery was well known and we had heard whispers of his famous Red Velvet Swing and the young show girls seduced in his private chamber at Madison Square Garden. But the appreciation of the art trumped the condemnation of the artist: Stanford White simply was *the best*. I had been impatient to contact him about work on the "island house" plans I had in my head, but first I had to secure the location. Then, before I could reach him, the shocking tragedy occurred.

We saw the dreadful news in the paper, the screaming headlines from the *New York Times* on June 26, 1906: "Thaw Murders Stanford White, Murders Him on the Roof of the Madison Square Garden."[98] The newspaper went on to describe the gory details of Harry K. Thaw's audacious firing of the pistol at close range into the head of the single diner Mr. White, attending a gala theatre evening at Madison Square Garden. For Harry Thaw, who had detectives following Stanny for months, it was the final "revenge killing" of the promiscuous architect who had a few years earlier seduced his wife, actress and artists' model Evelyn Nesbit, a young girl of sixteen, and then deserted her. Mr. White lay in his own blood while police quickly apprehended the glassy-eyed gunman and took him off to jail.

In the days following, all of the New York papers were regaling us with the licentious behavior of Stanny and some of his artist friends, pointing out the New York rendezvous studios and apartments which were used to photograph pubescent show girls. Rather sadly, Spencer and I thought, in the midst of yellow journalism the renown "creator" Stanny, the darling of society, the famed artist and inspired orchestrator of extravagant entertainment and opulent buildings had succumbed to an "under-life" of terrible choices in the company of society playboys and derelicts. He was vilified, his astonishing talent and accomplishments forgotten, his legacy scarred by his scandalous end. The dramatic trial would follow, and the wealthy Mr. Thaw was sent to a mental institution. (Later, Harry Thaw would be released, and would send scouts looking for a villa on Lake George, but that is another story.)

In the winter of 1906-07, while the Thaw trial mesmerized New York, Spencer and I had to look to our builders to follow through with the design details of our Triuna. The other was a hideous incident to put well behind us. I wrote in my journal that one of "the most valuable lessons I have learned is that, in a large measure, beauty and possibility lie in our own hands."[99] We would make this raw material of Triuna something beautiful for ourselves and useful for others as well. Perhaps artists might come here, too, for creative inspiration. Another sort of "trial-run" for Pine Garde's destiny after our deaths. There is always a higher purpose to be served in any of one's plans and I was certain I could create real beauty here for our family, friends, and artists. A diary entry that summer read:

"Choose beauty instead of convention and space instead of social correctness, a wide area for self-expression, even if WILD, instead of the smug and the finished, with hopeless limitations."[100]

This very idea had been at the core of our choosing

the location of our Yaddo, in the wilds of a pine forest instead of the fashionable avenues of Saratoga's North Broadway. Broadway was "the better investment," according to our senior friends: it was the location of society and all the latest trends. And there, Spencer and I noted to ourselves, lay the very reason for our choice. Now we shut out the world and its problems and concentrated on plans for the island world of the Trasks. Towards the end of next summer, the island home was completed to our taste, according to our special wishes, and enthusiastically described in all the papers. It was unique, and we had created it. That summer we "tented"again, this time on Triuna, while the structures were being completed. Then merrily we set about enjoying our new spaces by late August, entertaining a few close friends and numerous groups of young artists from New York who were greatly inspired by the views and the whole concept of our island.

As fate seemed to have it, Spencer and I *together* would have only three summers at Triuna. Two beautiful ones. One agonizing one in 1909.

Back at Yaddo my eye problems were still with me, but cheerful correspondence from friends at home and abroad brightened my outlook. And praise for my writings became more prevalent. This correspondence and my literary acceptance helped in many ways to save me from despair. My book *Night and Morning* had been well received in London, I was told, and was "much the talk of London drawing rooms as any book lately published."[101] The British critics liked my portrayal of Christ's forgiving nature with the sinning woman, and the idea of the spirit of the law being more important than the letter of the law. My religious beliefs dramatized Christ understanding Man's humanity and being able to forgive rather than condemn.

I was recently getting such positive response for other works of mine, some of which I had published anonymously in England and only now were being "discovered" at home, along with my authorship. One British critic thought my King Arthur play must have been written by a British author, so well did it define the King's nature. It seemed I had a lifetime of writing to do, so much to share with the world, and I shuddered at the thought of losing my eyesight. Suppose I should become totally blind? (Shut out the thoughts. Do not dare to travel that path.) I was also heartened by letters from Bishop Doane in Albany: Though I had lost my outer sight for a short time, my "inner sight was never dimmed," he kindly wrote.[102] When the eyesight was at its worst, I relied on Allena for my reading and writing. Allena was moonlight, sunlight, sister, and friend. Then would come periods of improvement in the eyesight, and it was as if a rainbow had appeared. All was promising again.

And with the new year of 1907 I did indeed feel hope, but the promise of the new year was a hollow one for many, as the Panic of 1907 brought financial ruin to institutions and individuals, ordinary people and those of great wealth. The Panic created some worried days for the Spencer Trask firm. Both partners were put to the test to preserve client wealth and to find safe havens and opportunities for the money entrusted to them. Spencer and Foster had much of their personal fortunes earmarked for their philanthropies, and steadfast vigilance and some clever financial maneuvering were called for if their commitments were to be honored.

Spencer was not a speaker of doom: he spoke brightly of my writing. He would not dwell on financial matters in my presence. I was kept from knowing the real truth of our financial peril because Spencer always sought to protect me. On one of my bleakest days back in 1906 he with his innate optimism had rescued me from utter despair. I had been in my tower room, sitting alone, not having the heart to call Allena for the typewriter to take down my thoughts. Earlier I had even bandaged the eyes and practiced walking as a blind person, feeling my way about the room. I had stumbled against a box of papers left by the bed and nearly fallen. This in my OWN room. HOW would I manage in an unfamiliar place?

"Today, my love, I bring you a miracle," he announced that afternoon, entering my sitting room with hands behind his back. *"I was going through some papers in my bank vault when I discovered something truly wonderful there. Something, my queen, which I had thought destroyed years ago in the first Yaddo's fire."*

With cloudy eyes I strained to see what he had brought. He came nearer and I felt him hand me something long: a rod, a stick... a *scepter*. My scepter from the coronation of Katrina Regina, the "naming ceremony" he had staged many years ago, which now was part of life at Yaddo and the origin of my official pen name.

Ugly and black it had been, he said, and it had survived its worst fate.

"Don't you see, my love? It couldn't be destroyed. It was tested by ugly flames, it 'lay in that vortex of flame and heat, that delicate bit of ivory'...and it survived.[103] Truly this is an omen for us. You have many more creative days to reign and to write, my love. There is more to come, Katrina. You will see. You are not to die. You will not be a derelict. There is much, much more to come."

And he took me in his arms, his strong arms. Yes, I *would* go on and on, creating until I died. My troubled life was surely marked with miracles with such a staunch and supportive husband at my side.

Despite the financial panic of 1907, by 1908 the summer colony on Lake George with Spencer and Foster at the helm was hard at work planning its new social club. The men were sports minded, most played golf and tennis and owned boats, and they delighted in competition and social intercourse among their own kind. They desired a club more private, a place more exclusive than the big hotels like the Sagamore or the Fort William Henry which were the social centers for short-term summer visitors. The residents of *our* Lake George summer colony included an elite collection of energetic, talented and successful individuals who sparked one another and accomplished quickly and adeptly tasks which seemed impossible to most. They were men from legal, financial, and business backgrounds willing to put up the money in advance, guarantee the club's early deficiencies, and to find more subscribers later. Men like W.

K. Bixby, George Owen Knapp, Herman Broesel, John Boulton Simpson, and Spencer and Foster who were doers and knew how to move mountains to reach their goals.

Spencer and Foster had been scouting proper locations for building such a club and ultimately, with input from other like-minded residents, settled on some property north of Diamond Point for purchase. Foster's favorite nephew, the talented Charles Samuel Peabody, had graduated from Harvard, Columbia, and the Paris Beaux-Arts with distinction, and he was hired out of New York city to design the Lake George Club. Within eleven months the club would be complete, including the building, tennis courts, golf course, and dock. The doors would open officially on August 14, 1909, but the club's first president Spencer Trask would be absent.

That August Spencer would be confined by pain behind drawn curtains at Triuna, suffering but forever cheerful and unresentful. A dreadful automobile accident had just cost him his eye, and almost his life. But overseeing the building of the gracious Tudor-style building with its magnificent terrace on the rocks had been a happy endeavor for my husband during the months before the accident. The story of the accident I will relate later in my tale of the devastating year 1909 which brought down a curtain on the first part of my life.

The other island in Lake George which held special meaning for me from the days of my youth was, of course, Diamond Island, farther south down the lake and nearer to Ed Shepard's Erlowest. It was a small island, but blessed with a picturesque shore and tall leafy trees and so named because of its quartz found there, quartz sparkling like diamonds. Diamond Island was steeped in American colonial history, used as a storage facility for weapons, and was a part of the landscape of the French and Indian War. Fierce battles had been fought in the area among enemy Indian tribes, and it was thought they had smoked the pipe of peace here finally. Ed Shepard and Foster conspired in the most wonderful way to offer a surprise gift to their friend. They knew how much I loved the island, and because of my interests in peace and in our staying away from foreign wars and entanglements, they thought of it as a place to be dedicated to the notion of Peace. They purchased the island.

One day Foster's *Pocahontas* met me in the village, its gay yellow smokestack and canopy contrasting with the large stands of red roses banking both sides of one of the deck chairs. Once I was settled ceremoniously in my chair, off we went, heading north, gliding over the silky waters. We were in Venice, we were in a gondola, drifting along blissfully toward Abenia, and then, surprisingly, we went on farther north, to Diamond Island.

Then it was presented to me, a gift to a peace-seeker, an island dedicated to the proposition of Peace. Assuming great court etiquette, Foster handed me a quite official looking document. *Will you accept this deed?* He and Edward had long been trying to secure the island for me, he confessed, and now it was mine.[104] My Arcadia, here with wildflowers crowding about my feet. After a walk-about we returned to Abenia where I found on the welcoming table in the hall yet another gift, a luscious diamond ring, to mark my "wedding to the island." And after that Edward gave me another stone, the giant towering rock brought down a mountainside and hauled to Diamond Island with great effort. It would become the obelisk on the northern end of the island on which we had carved across the face these words: "Peace, here the conqueror of many wars: 1666-1777." On either side of the statue, words of Peace were written in French and English.

Almost immediately, I decided to offer the island to the public, to everyone, to all people visiting Lake George. I vowed to make the island a peaceful stop for *all* boaters, and Spencer ordered the construction of a dock, picnic tables, a covered pavilion, restrooms. This island of my "awakening years of adolescence" I dedicated in the name of peace to all who would pause on Diamond Island and find rest. I believe Christina smiles for me in that decision. ✿

Two views of the Lake George Club, circa 1909.
{ Courtesy Centennial Committee of the
Lake George Club's *A Family of Friends: The First Hundred
Years at the Lake George Club, 1909-2009* }

Fuller House at Wiawaka, east side of Lake George.
{ Courtesy Wiawaka Holiday House }

Spencer Trask, far upper right, with guests on the porch
at Triuna Island, Lake George, circa 1908.
{ Courtesy Pat and Dick Swire }

Opposite above:
Gothic belfry and Triuna bridge.
{ Photo by the author }

Middle and lower:
The colonnaded bridges of Triuna Island, circa 1908.
{ Courtesy Pat and Dick Swire }

Chapter Five

Accidents Change Things, 1909

My husband loved the new-fangled automobiles. He often proclaimed that he was the first in New York to own one. In fact, back in 1900 he had purchased the Keystone Motor Company of Philadelphia with another man Mr. Search when they saw financial potential in the evolving automobile.[105] They renamed it the Searchmont Motor Company and soon hired a Frenchman with a racing car background to design for them. Mr. Fournier's design led to a powerful motor car that was outpacing the competition, but the Panic of '07 forced Spencer to pull in his horns (everyone was blue, he said, about the future) and withdraw his financial support for the company.

Still Spencer loved those autos, and was always trying out different models for the right one for his trips around Saratoga, up to Glens Falls and to the lake. His favorite car was his very first one, the Red Devil, the sports car which daringly he drove at break-neck speed, ten miles per hour, rounding the curved roads of the driveway with reckless abandon.[106] He had foreseen the day when everyone would own personal automobiles and in 1908 had begun construction of a large garage at Yaddo with living quarters above where our guests' drivers might stay when meetings or conferences were held at our home. He also wanted a personal garage with its own gas pump, and it must be fire-proof, he demanded. It was to be three stories and have ample storage area for horse-drawn carriages, plus a stable area for horses, as these would still be useful for several years.[107]

In June of 1909, Spencer was in Boston on business and I was at Yaddo when I received news of the terrible crash of Spencer's car with a trolley car. The city of Boston those days was a transportation nightmare of horse-drawn carriages, trolley cars and the new autos, and Spencer, ever on the edge of new technology, had chosen to go about the city by auto that day, and so hired a car and driver from a local rental company. He had attended a play north of town with others, and was returning when the accident occurred. Spencer was in the passenger seat and had a devastating injury to his face from the broken glass, in particular a blow and a gash to his eye. He might lose his complete sight if the eye were not removed I was told, and here I was, helplessly confined to rest at home at the time.

I was not well, could not come to him, and for weeks while he remained in a Boston hospital, we corresponded, my letters and telegrams full of encouragement and support, his own full of optimism and fear for the effect of his accident on me

"Good morning, my love. I am with you every minute in all but body," my telegram said.[108]

"I have some very nice nurses whose voices only I

have heard. *Please carry out the plans of moving to the lake next week entirely independent of me. The doctor tells me that I shall have to stay here some weeks. I do not believe it, and since you know my general determination to have my own way, I shall be home much sooner.*"[109]

The manager of the Somerville Automobile Company was of course concerned about his liability in the accident. He wrote asking *"do you consider it my driver's fault or the fault of the electric* [car]?"[110]

Spencer answered that *"your man was at fault."* He was obviously drinking *"enough to make him garrulous but not drunk enough to make me unwilling to run the risk of his taking us home."*[111]

We were not so interested in lawsuits over automobile accidents. Earlier we had dealt with a frivolous suit brought against Spencer when his car did not stop after witnessing a man fall getting off a trolley in Glens Falls. It was charged that Spencer's driver actually hit the man. It was a long and arduous procedure to have the matter put aside (though we did pay a sum to the injured man) and to have Spencer's name exonerated. NEVER would Spencer have left the scene of an accident where someone had been injured, and ALWAYS would he take the blame if he had erred. Spencer and his driver had seen the "injured man" get right up after falling from the trolley and they had assumed he was uninjured. And they of course had NEVER hit the man with their car.

We just did NOT want to get involved in yet another lawsuit. So unpleasant to deal with these matters. It pleased me to hear of Spencer's unselfish and spontaneous act of bravery in Boston when his car was about to be struck by the trolley. He had evacuated the other passengers and tried to get the car pushed out of the way to avoid the head-on crash. *"Did you think you would die when you saw the trolley coming,"* I asked him later? *"No time to be afraid,"* he had said. *"There was no time to do anything but get the car pushed sufficiently aside to avoid a total head-on collision."* So indicative of my husband: there was "a carload of passengers to be saved" and he just did it, the hero and the only one to be injured that evening.

My husband never felt sorry for himself, never complained, and was a model of bravery and strength during that summer in Boston. After two operations, the injured eye still in place, Spencer eventually came home to me on our island mid-summer to rest. Spencer knew he had to face the eventual need to have the eye removed to save the sight in his good eye. Our surgeon from New York would be summoned to Triuna on that ghastly mission; it was a horrid agonizing day for us both and sometimes I awake, haunted by the dreadful image of the assault on his eye.

All this happened while plans were being unveiled for the gala opening of the Lake George Club on August twelvth. With the vision, perseverance, and financial might of Spencer, Foster, W. K. Bixby and thirteen other club incorporators, the design, construction, and completion of the clubhouse, tennis courts, and golf course had happened in an amazing eleven-month period. Using the local bank, local contractors, and the financial clout of the incorporators, the Lake George Club — a grand presence in its imposing berth on the rocks, with its paint-erly views up and down the lake — was opened to its enthusiastic members with great fanfare.

Some friends later came to visit and commiserate with Spencer, and left marveling at his unflappable opti-mism and cheerfulness. I know how he suffered in those days, but he insisted on music in the house and on hear-ing stories of the events at the newly-opened club. He set up a cup for the winner of the end-of-season tennis tournament held there. He would not allow his friends to speak of his ordeal.

Looking back on the year 1909 now I think of only tragedy upon tragedy, but a bright spot was the successful production of my play *Little Town of Bethle-hem* staged at Brooklyn's Academy of Music, benefiting Hampton Institute. It had been so well received, a dif-ferent Nativity play where the Virgin and little Christ Child are never on stage. I was pleased to be able to sug-gest without really portraying directly the majesty and glory of the Child and to represent different civiliza-tions through characters, civilizations which ironically would fall before the might of the divine Child. It was produced elsewhere, too, and I was very proud of the power of the play and its popularity.

But perhaps this early January joy was my only lasting happiness in 1909. Spencer's auto accident in the summer foreshadowed the Other Tragic Accident, the one which would burst upon us on New Year's Eve and shatter my life. That event on December thirty-first came as an obscene blow after much gathering of faith and sheer will to get on with out lives and duties after a daunting summer of pain. It came during the holiday season we loved the most, and it came down on the Trask family with hideous irony.

We had left the island and returned to Yaddo in the fall of 1909 with stiff upper lip and an agenda. Spencer was busy overseeing the new garage and tending to business of the Saratoga Reservation Commission, a project he had taken on with great enthusiasm. He was working hard with our attorney and friend Edward Shepard in New York, hoping to come up with some suggestions for preserving the mineral springs from over use and over-commercialization. He had studied spas from Europe and had creative ideas for protecting the waters and making Saratoga Springs a grand and beautiful spa-resort. His final report was to be the first agenda for the New York State Assembly in the new year and had to be approved by Ed before then. Spencer's concept of duty was to be his downfall.

But first, God granted Spencer and me the beautiful first days of our traditional Christmas celebration at Yaddo, a celebration lasting a full week leading up to Twelfth Night. It was the high point, the supreme culmination of all that was unique and spiritual at the place: it defined the essence of our estate. Yaddo was festooned with garlands of pine and white roses. There was holly on the carved mantels, the smell of holiday cinnamon and cider wafting from the kitchen, and light-hearted merriment among the servants. The holiday was theirs, too, and they looked forward to opening the double doors to Servants' Hall where each family had personal gifts and a decorated tree.

From my sitting room for days now I had enjoyed hearing the rehearsals for the upcoming pageant: Amy's clear soprano voice, the deep bass of Tommy, the higher, sweeter angelic tones of the younger children, and the strong and dramatic voice of Spencer rehearsing the reading of the Christmas story. The servants were in awe of Spencer and the dramas he scripted for Yaddo's Christmas days. It pleased me greatly that they, our large and wonderful family, loved Spencer... and me, so much, and that we could give back to them a "sense of family" and an appreciation of the beautiful and the artistic in life. The annual Christmas concert of carols with all of us singing would be just as beautiful this year. None of us *ever* suspected it would be the last Christmas for Spencer.

Already we had been in rehearsal for the Twelfth-Night festival, a pageant most beautiful and elaborate, a tradition we had enjoyed at Yaddo since 1899. Spencer and I had inaugurated it on January 6th that year as a carnival with ancient pageantry and revelry to celebrate the fellowship enjoyed in our home. It involved the entire household plus invited friends, and included horns and court jesters and white doves and wassail bowls, and rehearsed songs celebrating the Yule log brought in ceremoniously and set ablaze in the hearth. It was a celebration of the spirit of peace and fellowship among all of us, uniting those who serve with those who are served. "The strength and honor of a house, as well as its ornament, are the friends who frequent it," we liked repeating. And so in this spirit of expectancy, hope, good cheer, tradition, and love we found the revels ended with a crushing blow... before they were even begun. In 1909 there would be no Twelfth-Night celebration.

"No school-boy ever dreaded to go to school in Holiday time more than he dreaded to go to New York. It was the supreme octave of our Yaddo year," I wrote in my journal. *"With us the Christmas always lasted from December twenty-third to Twelfth Night. Everything at Yaddo was at its height of festivity and joy. The chimes were ringing every day, the servants were singing their carols, and all was buoyant."*[112]

It was a snowy night, and the cold hurt Spencer's sensitive eye, and so I wanted to say no. No, don't go out in this dreadful weather to New York tonight. Not tonight. But I said yes. Yes, I think you should go. Because I knew he felt it was his *duty* to get those ideas to Edward in the city in order to meet the deadline of the legislative session in the new year. I said yes, and gave him a cheerful kiss. He knew all along he would be going. (I wonder, now, if he was not like Jesus going to Jerusalem, knowing his fate.) He closed the door of a home warm with a convivial fire blazing at the hearth and the heavenly smell of pine, and he walked out into the cold on the thirtieth of December.

He boarded with briefcase the Montreal *Express* from Saratoga, and sat in the train for several hours due to bad weather conditions in up-state New York. Finally he was underway, comfortable in the luxury of a private car with sleeping berths in the rear where he could review his plans in privacy. The train barreled its way south, making up for lost time, until it reached a signal to stop, somewhere south of Croton, New York. There it sat, with its engineer unaware that an express freight train from Vancouver, loaded with valuable silk, pulling eight cars and a caboose behind it, was hurtling southward. It saw no signal to stop. The freight train forged ahead at full speed until the last moments when it suddenly saw the stopped Montreal *Express* three hundred feet ahead.

The *New York Times* reported that at eight o'clock on the morning of New Year's Eve Spencer Trask had become, unbelievably, the only fatality in a train wreck caused by a freight train running its signal (or not seeing a signal), and plunging, beastly wrenching steel and gouging splintered wood, into the calmness of his car. The pictures of the mangled wreckage in the *Times* on January 1, 1910, were ghastly. Though a few others were injured, Spencer was the only to die instantly of a concussion to the head, "in the act of dressing, putting on his shoes."[113] They had to pry open his car, telescoped up the middle into the next car, and pull him from underneath collapsed berths.[114] Amazingly, he showed no visible death-blows, but his skull had been fractured.

They had found papers and identification, and the note, worn and folded neatly in his pocket: "For a man's worth consisteth not in the abundance of his possessions." (That was, and will ever be, the *shibboleth* of my husband.) Spencer's worth, as I was to discover soon after, lay not in financial wealth, but in his thoughts and actions for others. He had been on a mission for other men on New Year's Eve. During the grim recovery process, railroad officials had been surprised to learn that their one fatality was the foremost financier Spencer Trask, president of the prestigious Spencer Trask firm and noted patron of the arts. The New York Central Railroad sent his body home to me in Saratoga in a special car, after it was claimed by my brother Acosta Nichols, the family member who was closest to Croton and the scene of the accident.

I recall the next few days as surreal scenes of remembered joy with Spencer, then yelping stabs of pain at the thought of life without him. I saw images of Spencer, his lifeless body bent, wedged beneath a berth of shredded leather and splintered wood. I saw images of Spencer, tall and elegant, on horseback, surveying the rows of roses in my garden. I saw Spencer with a face of blood and gore on a Boston trolley track. I saw my husband in medieval costume, in sweeping bow, handing me a scepter on my "queen's coronation." He had given me my pen name Katrina, and he had been my greatest literary supporter. ANGER, I felt then, anger that this sweet and noble man on a mission for others should be the only person singled out by the serpent of death, snatched away from a full and worthy life.

Why of *all people* Spencer? Unjust. And then I realized it was my great loss, it was *my* husband sent home lifeless in a box on those same dastardly rails from Hell, to leave me alone and un-guided. Who would entice the smiles when I was suffering, who would bring the light of positive thinking when I was battling dim vision, who would be there for ME? Selfish, I know, but it was *my* loss, above all others' loss. So many shared moments, shared visions and plans, gone.

The house felt vastly empty. The house itself was mocking me, Katrina Trask, now alone here with all my family taken from me. I could not fall asleep for any length of time. I felt my body was shrinking, the windows and walls moving inward to envelop me. I felt devoured by the framework of Yaddo, the place built as a dream for our family and then a dream for creative people everywhere. I cried out in anguish, and asked for my own death. I felt there was no energy or resolve left within to continue. I had no strength or will to re-arm for battle alone against the dark forces which seemed always at my heel. For the first day and a half I had no strength to rise from my bed. And my physical limitations exacerbated the abject grief I felt, increased my sense of slowly disappearing into the silk folds of my bed sheets.

Ever attentive to my needs was Alenna with her cups of fresh tea on my favorite china tray... and the almond biscuits from cook's kitchen. Alenna with her smiling face and soothing hands rubbing my temples until I fell asleep for a little while. Alenna with a fresh vase of evergreens and camellias from the greenhouse and her notebook of lists of those who had called or offered condolences. She knew I would be precise about acknowledging these kindnesses in the ensuing days. She knew she could see me through this.

Now downstairs here at Yaddo was Foster, working at Spencer's desk in the study, organizing the cremation and interment in Brooklyn at Greenwood Cemetery. Spencer's will had left him in control, along with me. There would be memorial services later. I had made the effort to go downstairs on the second day, and quietly opening the library door I had discovered Foster head down on his crossed arms, shoulders shuddering with sobs. He had lost his best friend, his partner, his Brother-in-Arms. I had turned and left him to his private sorrow.

This time I stood quietly at the doorway to Spencer's library for some time, until Foster looked up from his papers and rose to come to me. His eyes were bleary and his beautiful white thick hair seemed uncharacteristically disheveled.

"My old companion Grief has returned," I managed, straining through tears.

"And he visits me, as well, my darling Lady."

My arms went around him, and he, in turn, held me so fiercely, with such need, that I found myself the consoler, the strength. It was just the two of us now, two of us to plan the tributes to our fallen comrade, to take the helm of the firm, to follow through with all of Spencer's plans and commitments and dreams. There in Spencer's study, we decided that together we would be up to the task at hand. I also knew, so clearly now, encircled in these arms, that I would never be alone. Spencer had left me in the tender care of his best friend. With this knowledge the first ray of sunshine came into my life, but that ray could not make me strong enough to be allowed to leave Yaddo for the services. The doctors had taken stewardship of my life.

Spencer's funeral service was held on January third at our local church, Bethesda Episcopal, in Saratoga Springs. Attending were mourners throughout the town and from Yaddo, and including the girls from St. Christina's and notables from New York. But Mrs. Trask was not in attendance. My body would not permit. But my spirit did travel heavily to church with the cortege departing from Yaddo, a sad procession moving down the drive and onto Union Avenue, along this street into town amidst the sound of bells chiming from all the churches in town, sixty-six chimes for the years of his life on earth. Foster's and my plan was to have his body cremated and sent down to Greenwood Cemetery, where he would be interred next to his four children and his beloved father Alanson. The *New York Times* ran various tributes and announcements of Spencer's life and gifts over the next days and noted the upcoming memorial service which would be held in New York. Like his funeral, the memorial service for Spencer in New York was held without me at the Church of the Ascension, Fifth Avenue and Tenth Street, on Saturday afternoon, January 29, 1910. The service was arranged by and held under the direction of the National Arts Club, of which Spencer had been president at the time of his death. The church was decorated in evergreens, his beloved pine, and was filled with prominent representatives of the world of politics, art, business, the church, the town of Saratoga Springs, and even some of the sisters of the St. Christina School. The next day the rector of Bethesda Church in Saratoga would give his expectant congregation an account of the memorial service; the *Saratoga Sun* also would include in great detail the program planned for Spencer so that all of his friends could be a part of the last tribute.

At the memorial service, New York Governor Charles Evans Hughes had set the tone: the motto of Spencer Trask was "to do what is right and to serve your fellow man." My dear Henry van Dyke's tribute noted that Spencer's *"worth is the greater because his character shone through in his business world, his wholesome current of life stood out amidst activities of cunning and multiplicity of sordid concerns."* He lauded our making of Yaddo a shared place thrown open to the public, not closed in by private walls, a place *"designed not to dazzle or oppress the guests, but to welcome them and to cheer them."*

He voiced what Spencer and I believed deeply: to fulfill God's will is to be *"human in our lives: in our touch with others, in our service for others, to give not only with the hand but of the heart, to give not only from the purse but from the love, and to live with others as we would have others live with us, in fellowship, in kindness, in friendship, in love, in mutual help."* [115]

The Reverend Percy Grant, rector of the Church of the Ascension, noted that Spencer was *"a business man, and an artist. He made an art of life, caring for dignity, harmony, decorum, for measure. He associated with those who speed the material machinery of life and who provide for the progress of physical civilization, but he kept company with beautiful souls who were intent upon the discovery of the eternal loveliness of creation."* [116]

Our friend Edward Shepard, too, spoke of Spencer the artist and asserted that his was *"not esoteric devotion to art for art's sake but art as a means of human benefaction. He did everything with the belief that the beautiful must conquer... how he loved color and grace of form...*

and his life, in fact, was a fabric, rich and beautiful which he made for others."[117] Later, when I discovered there was not much fortune left in the Trask Estate, I found solace in another part of Edward's tribute: *"He did not reap harvests taken from other men who had earned them. If the harvest came to him, none was poorer for that. The making of money was for him, only a calling, subordinate to his many other activities. For him, the use of money was to make more abundant his own life and the lives of others."*[118]

Though I sat that January day in my tower room at Yaddo, I could hear clearly in my mind's place the Brahms piece "How Lovely Is The Dwelling Place"; the "Ave Maria" by Gounod-Bach; Bizet's "Agnus Dei"; and Wagner's "Awake!" sung by the church choir. I could feel the love of our friends traveling up to me at Yaddo. And I could feel the special spirituality which Spencer and I shared in our religious views, views which were not really anti-establishment views, but which embraced and included traditional views, the ardent support of our churches, and then went beyond into the Universe. Spencer's and my religion was larger than the Church. I wrote in his funeral book this:

"The freedom and vigor of his soul knew no barriers of sect or of tradition. He hated dogma: he rebelled against articles or canons, with all the protest of his spacious nature! But Christ was His Master and His Lord and there was a magnificent faith within Him, vital, universal, cosmic."[119]

I remembered last summer's fading August days with Spencer confined to his darkened room at Triuna. Repeatedly he was singing this verse, sometimes overly dramatically, sometimes laughingly:

"Conduct me Zeus, and Thou O Destiny;

Wherever thy decrees Have fixed my lot, I follow cheerfully."[120]

But Spencer, I had interjected, you are addressing a Pagan God.

"Are they Pagan, Kate? In essence they are the same as 'Guide Me Oh Thy Great Jehovah'... or 'Thy Will Be Done.' It is what we all must do, follow the Everlasting God... Zeus... Jupiter... Jehovah... god... call Him what you will. Follow and work the work that waits to be done... follow through whatever comes... led by the Hand that shapes the path... the Greeks called it Destiny... we call it the Will of God,... but it is the same in reality. We must follow, and [he added with his IRRESISTIBLE smile] *if we follow, we might as well follow cheerfully."*[121]

Looking through some of Spencer's papers in the next few days I found a slip of paper, yellow with age, but bearing the date of a time when we were full of anxiety and stress. I would hold this verse in my heart and take it to my own grave:

"The Lord is nigh unto all them
that call upon Him faithfully.
He will fulfill the desires of them that Fear Him.
He also will hear their cry and will help them.
The Lord preserveth all them that love Him."

You see? I was not deserted at all. Not by Spencer and not by the Lord. I repeated this verse daily for a long while. But I knew also that going on without Spencer's guidance and influence would require great courage.

Chapter Six

Life After Spencer

After Spencer's death I knew I could not write again. I had been on the edge of a most interesting literary career but after Spencer's death I told Macmillan and Company I would not be writing another book. For two years I would do nothing literary except dictate letters to kind friends who had sent condolences and compile a *Memorial Book* of my husband for close friends and family. This would contain funeral eulogies, speeches, poems, letters of condolence, and writings which I felt best honored Spencer's life. I included my own address which was read at his memorial service, and my later dedication of our library at Yaddo as a living memorial to Spencer:

"In the library of Yaddo the home life has always centered and flamed, and when the Master of the House went out I closed the doors, and knew that if they were ever opened it must be to dedicate the room to some living purpose in memory of him. Today the doors are opened once again. Henceforth the room is to be used for the educational help of the young people of Saratoga. I desire to have lecturers for graduates of the high school and for the senior class, on such subjects as shall be indicated to me by those who are

in charge of the High School."[122]

During the first year or so there were frightening financial matters needing my attention in order to preserve the future design for Yaddo. There was surprisingly little wealth left in Spencer's estate. He had given most to his philanthropies. We had lived a life of ease and plenty, nurturing our tastes and inclinations with ease, but we were never at the financial level of the other titans of business we knew in New York. My social conscience now begs the question of how I could feel "poor." Wealth was a matter of relativity: my position was a giant step above that of most in our country. And yet this sense of impoverishment shook me to the core, because I feared for the future of Yaddo. We discussed changing some of the details of the plans for the artists' retreat, such as reducing the number of guests, and possibly the number of months that the house would be open. I was shaken by the needs I saw ahead, but I had Foster's keen business mind to guide me. We added more trustees to Pine Garde, my two brothers George and Acosta, and also my nephew Edwin. The new board spent a great deal of time addressing our needs and coming up with solutions.

To compound matters, there was a reoccurrence of my heart troubles and we had to call my doctor up from New York to consult with our Saratoga doctor. It was serious. The doctor said I must "go into the shadow" if I was to preserve my eyesight, so much of the time was spent away from sunlight and strenuous activity. Already the vision was gone in one eye. Were the Trasks to be plagued with eye issues, we who wanted to read, to write, to do so much with our eyes? I prayed for patience and acceptance, and persevered.

Then, my reader, miracles DID happen for me some time after that.

First, my writing career did in fact come back, in full force and with great impact. Once again, when I needed it most, an inspiration came to me. Suddenly one night the scenes for a book came faster than I could record them to the page... I was aflame with inspiration, characters, concrete images... and I was writing through the day and through the night. I was obsessed with the writing of it, filled with the emotions of the characters, burning with the message. Such was the birth of my book which would come to be the most influential of all my works: *In the Vanguard*.

It usually took me a year for a literary piece to be finished, to do the polishing and rewriting, but I did this book in record time and sent it out to the good people in the publishing world. How surprised I was to find a sympathetic ear, in fact, great enthusiasm. They passed it on, and "it seemed to catch fire," this piece on peace, this play on the ugliness of war, this plea for pacifism. Next year I would write the script for the play, and later on it would be produced across America, in high-schools, in churches, and at some political rallies. There would be eight editions. And this pacifist play would be followed by essays and poems in a host of magazines and newspapers which earned me the title of Pacifist and Peace Lady.

In the Vanguard presented Elsa and Philip as my young characters, full of romantic notions of the glory of war, she wanting a war hero, he wanting to "rescue the oppressed." I didn't want the message to overshadow the drama, to create the character as flat spokesman for the view without believable emotion. I wanted the ugliness and horror of death and dying, the stench of the battlefield to speak for itself. And I wanted to expose those who make Christ an apologist for war, twisting His words to suit a perverted cause. Elsa with glowing cheeks and eyes wants the brave fighter who will spill his blood for his country, but in the end she and her disillusioned soldier Philip are able to see who the real heroes are, those who serve the God of Peace. The true heroes are those who sacrifice self to service, the Scientists, the Educators, the Up-builders of the Nation, the Reformers... and those who refuse war because it breaks the law of harmony and love in the world.

It came as a surprise to no one, my strong views about war. In 1898 when the *Times* and other newspapers had hinted at the "inevitability" of a war with Spain over Cuba, I had been outraged. I had written an editorial in support of a Harvard professor who tried to dissuade young men from volunteering in a ridiculous and barbaric fight. The professor had dared to suggest war was foolishness, and was subsequently barraged with insulting remarks and censure by newspapers and "patriotic" men ready to liberate Cuba. The Hearst and Pulitzer newspapers in particular supported a war and used emotional language, "yellow journalism," to built popular support for a war declaration against Spain. Spanish mistreatment of Cubans was painted in "large language." The newspapers had stated that the U. S.

must avenge the destruction of the battleship the *U. S. S. Maine* which had exploded in Havana harbor, evidently a victim of Spanish sabotage. It was said Mr. Pulitzer had sent the reporter Frederic Remington to cover the war when it finally erupted, telling him "You supply the pictures, I'll supply the war."

I had written this response to the professor's censure after he spoke out against the war in an editorial:

"If someone feels war is wrong and barbaric, then he should be allowed to say it. Sometimes those writing for peace are the WISEST men of all, the bravest men, in fact, not the men heading off to war," I had maintained, *"And the judge of who is the wisest is not made by the impassioned verdict of the hour."*

I wrote "Humanity Versus Humanity" at the beginning of the short four-month conflict. And the ideals expressed here would serve me again as we tottered at the edge of World War I. The same sentiment, another war.

"We have shone among the nations
as a light set on a hill;
They could keep their standing armies,
they could fight, and rend and kill;
Round the world the whirr of battles
might tremble and increase,
But we were strong in quietness
and mighty in our peace.
Shall we quench that light in darkness,
and go back to other days?
Leave the larger Christian methods,

and return to heathen ways?
If now we fail to guard that trust,
that light upon the hill
Forget our revelation,
and again wage war and kill;
We may help a little island
in a corner of the earth
But the larger, true Humanity
will be strangled at its birth."
— April 1, 1898, Yaddo.

The U. S. Ambassador to Spain General Woodford actually spent some time at Yaddo, after he was sent home from Spain at the beginning of the war. He spent four days with us, he and his wife, as we followed the "heroic" events in Cuba and the exploits of the Rough-Rider, Mr. Roosevelt, as he carved out a name for himself. None of us at Yaddo that summer of 1898 was very enthusiastic as we watched a truly imperialistic war being waged under the flag of "moral duty."

While I was aflame with my pacifist writing in later years I corresponded with a German literary friend, Mr. J. M. Beck, whose delightful books on Michelangelo and Bach had so pleased me. I agreed with his own indignation over the Kaiser who recently, in the international press, had praised the bellicose words of a German poet. I was aghast that the Kaiser, supposedly the most enlightened and cultured monarch in Europe, was taking such an aggressive stance and, it appeared, was about to lead his country into war. Our own country felt itself coming to attention with each new affront and aggression in

Europe; we noted the alarming events and build up of tension in the Balkans, heard with horror the pugilistic words of the Kaiser, felt with pity the fears of the smaller nations in the paths of the greater ones.

My friends in Europe had kept me informed of the growing potential for a European war, of senseless secret pacts and the building up of national armies for aggressive moves on neighboring territories. Europe, for a number of years now, was a tinder box of entangling alliances, awaiting a provocation to explode into a world conflagration. Something had to be done to prevent the potential poison of war excitement across the Atlantic from infecting the Americans and pulling us in. I took the challenge with my only weapon, the pen... and some social and literary and political connections. I could show with real characters and their real emotions what war could do to human beings and how it never solved disagreements among people.

A bit later I would lobby for peace in letters to President Wilson, but when we ultimately joined the ugly mess, and the United States in 1917 went to war, I personally would support the cause and have the Yaddo farm acreage yield forth its part for the war effort. In fact, I would close down Yaddo completely to save money for its future destiny, and would move out to live in the little cottage I had on the property. The sooner the war was over, the sooner would come Peace. But I get ahead of myself.

I pause here, with some true reticence, to mention the second miracle which came after Spencer's death. The miracle was an important happening which I welcomed in the spirit of a fresh young maiden, not a lady of middle age and compromised body. During these years of heart trouble and dimming vision, with the requirement of rest, interminable rest, I did have a stretch of rare moments of pure, beautiful *HEALTH* when it seemed my life of frailty was over and I would be released to lead an abundant physical existence of freedom and pleasure.

That late spring month of lilacs was rare in my history of poor health, but it afforded me a chance to consider very seriously a wholly different path for my life. That path would be into the arms of my best friend Foster, as his lover and *wife*, as well as his business associate. Because Spencer and I had always believed in privacy and discretion, modesty begs me not to speak of more intimate details of my life, details seemingly "unfitting" for a true lady's memoir. But as I write the story of Yaddo and my life, as I have opened my heart here to you my readers, I will offer myself *totally*. I will show you a lady unveiled, perhaps compromised in your judgment for speaking unabashedly, but a lady as she was at a rare time of vibrant physical health experiencing a love affair so beautiful it must be recognized as significant to her biography. Simply said, I loved George Foster Peabody. I loved him completely. The sudden recognition of my passion for him was a shocking assault of romance in my fifty-sixth year. As I later looked back, it was a romance captured in eternity, like the figures on Keats' "Grecian Urn": she always fair and young and somehow elusive, he always pursuing her ardently. Our love was Keats' love whose beauty lay in its striving, the romantic quest caught in the beholder's imagination. But while our romance lived in the flesh, for just a little while, it flamed brighter, much brighter than this cold philosophical image.

I had listened to Foster's marriage proposals beginning some time after Spencer's death, though at first I protested too adamantly and found him recoiling into reticence, with absences from Yaddo for several days after the rebuffs. But when the curtain lifted, magical healthy optimistic days when I felt strong and alive with feeling, I stumbled upon the love affair of my life. Health allowed me to consider Love. And Marriage. Foster had been in my life forever, a close friend and fellow Romantic, and Spencer had often suggested a marriage to "the perfect one" if he should die before me. He knew how similar we were in temperament and outlook, and how Foster was a part of the vision for Yaddo. Foster and I together would guarantee the legacy of the place. But Spencer had not dreamed of the possibility of my discovering another Love because he was so secure in my love for him. And I never dreamed that for four weeks I would wake mornings, longing for the comfort of Foster's arms in my bed, for his lips, for his beautiful words, for all the exquisiteness of a physical relationship with this man I had possibly *always loved.*

Foster and I had four perfect weeks that seemed to

be leading to the decision of our marriage. We were full of plans, full of passion, overcome with the sweetness of being together as man and woman. There were days and nights of secret meetings when Allena was in New York for a few days, happy to see me self sufficient and full of robust health. God-gifted warm June afternoons alone at the top of Yaddo's highest hill, past the Stone Tower, with picnics and a soft quilt under the firs. Heloise and Abelard stealing a few hours of bliss (did we, even then, know these days of physical intimacy were numbered, and that ours, like theirs, was a tragic love story?)

Nights in my tower or in Foster's own room at Yaddo, after the servants had gone to bed, when we celebrated our love with all our passion. We were full of the titillation of being near one another next day amongst the household staff, together as we always had been, but now with our *secret* of the nights before. Under the spell of romance my wrinkled brow was smooth velvet, my hair shiny and luxurious, my body fresh and young and bursting with desire. Foster's eyes melted me in a shameless way. The hands which shyly brushed mine in the old days now boldly took charge of his caresses. Enchanted by his words, captive to his touch, nothing mattered but being with him, sharing with him, living in his space. My whole day hung in uneasy balance until he came near me, righting the universe and charging the air with the light of our love. My reader, it was a holy and *blessed captivity!*

We passed tender days so exhilarating and physically satisfying that when the heart trouble ruthlessly descended upon me again in full force, it was an ugly double blow. It destroyed my hopes for miraculous health and my dreams of a marriage to Foster. The Ghoul stood at my door and glowered, and I was reduced to my crushing decision. Foster Peabody, alive with bodily vigor, NEVER would be saddled with an invalid for a wife. We were cursed as thwarted lovers, and blessed as deepest friends. Keats' philosophy haunted me: *what is held in the memory and imagination is captured in time for eternity.* I would not desecrate the memory of our perfect days together with a physically wrecked heroine as wife, an invalid too *weighty* for a man *light* with energy and health. And so I closed that chapter. I turned to the next page, the next section in the story of my life.

You judge me now. Here, such a cold and unfeeling lady, mistress of control, mercurially igniting, then extinguishing all emotion. Reader, you must know that my decision was not as easy as it might appear, and that loss of "what might have been" for over a decade I wore as a hair-shirt, carefully hidden away but raw and painful. Life has chastened me. I am schooled to show no bitterness, but underneath the resolve and control is a mere woman, a frail soul ever reaching for what she may never attain. A small pilgrim on a journey of opening gates, pushing ahead undaunted... seeking love, happiness, and beauty in one's life. A journey to find purpose and meaning in each day's living. It is a universal pilgrimage I make with my fellow travelers — white satin and homespun, the grand lady and the least kitchen maid, the sculptor of marble and the dusty quarryman — and it might as well be a brave march. An appearance, a countenance, a certain seemliness is maintained along the way, but there is within each one of us a human heart which bears its own jagged scar.

✦

And what of Lake George and Triuna after Spencer's death?

After Spencer I made the move to Triuna for three more summers with my household staff, and managed to make it through the initial season without my husband. I had determined that lake living was beneficial to my mental and physical health: all the scientific evidence pointed to the healthful effect of sleeping in fresh air. One of my favorite summer evenings at Triuna involved a boatload of Wiawaka girls and a supervisor who were brought across the lake in Foster's *Pocahontas* for "an evening with the lady of the lake." They were delighted to arrive at Triuna with fairy lights twinkling in the trees of the island, medieval banners decorating the white tents. The girls were thrilled to partake of the supper prepared for them and the handing out of gifts for each one, along with copies of *The Secret Garden*, an enchanting new book from England. While propped up by pillows on the big white linen banquette in my tent, I read to the entire group assembled at my feet, each girl with her colored ribbon to designate her group for touring the islands. Their eyes were full of wonder, and none of us wished the evening to be over. Afterwards they sent to me a beautiful token of thanks, a china dish with Katrina pink roses hand-painted across its face. It is one of my dearest keepsakes.

But there were frightening events to occur at Triuna during my third summer at the lake without him. In August of 1912 I was awakened in the middle of the night to the bells ringing wildly from the belfry. I smelled smoke, and joined by our caretaker and Allena we saw from our southernmost quarters the flames licking over the *Pocahontas* moored on the north island, then engulfing the smaller boats. We watched dumbstruck as the household staff formed bucket-brigades and battled the encroaching flames moving towards their own sleeping rooms. In the end, God granted us the blessing of a change of winds, which saved the middle and southern islands.

Lights blinked on along the shoreline as neighbors heard the crackling of flames and the explosions from the tanks of the boats, and soon boats of neighbors from the shore were on their way to Triuna to help put out the fire. James and Arthur lifted me bodily from my quarters and literally ran to the first boat, a neighbor's, and secured my safety while the flames slowly were subdued. The belfry and colonnaded bridges were saved, as were our quarters, but my household lost everything. Shock overcame me as I neared the shore: I could feel my mouth forming wordless words. *Please save my family. My family.*

I was taken to Foster's Abenia to "recover" and then back to Yaddo, where I immediately made plans to rebuild what was lost, albeit at a modest investment, because my finances were becoming limited. My heart was vulnerable at this time, and more health setbacks followed soon after: I was not aware then that I was never again to return to my Venice on the Lake. Some time later my neighbor Mr. Bixby made a mild inquiry as to the "unseemly" facade of the new buildings on the north side. I had to explain that the work is "only begun... and that the kitchen was a hasty necessity."[123] *"I plan to put some arches around the building and to have the whole building covered with a quick-growing vine... so that it will be a great bank of green. We built in a straightforward manner with the North Island buildings arranged for convenience, mostly for storage. North Island is strictly for service. After all, the beauty is in the South and Middle Islands and the bridges."*[124] I decided in August of 1914 to write Mr. Bixby another letter, a discreet one asking for his valuation of Triuna, as I was fearful I would have to sell it.

"I doubt now if ever again I will be strong enough to live that delicious life in the open air," I wrote. *Would you be kind enough to give me some valuation to place on the islands? And would you keep this matter private?*[125] As it turned out, I did not sell Triuna, because I came around to the idea that it might be used, like Yaddo's future design, for artists and their creativity. But Mr. Bixby was a welcomed friend to Spencer and me, a man of such varied interests, unique talents and a discreet counselor regarding the lake.

In relating my story of the years just after the master went away, I want to share with you another sad story, this one a harrowing tale of lost dreams, which occurred earlier in the spring. I was personally saddened by the news event that stunned the world and made us all feel the transiency of life, perhaps even the foreshadowing of the end of our era. On April 15th, 1912, the brand new luxury ship *Titanic* was on its maiden voyage from Europe to America. It moved through the Atlantic regally, a bulk of tiered and lighted majesty, its luxurious suites in first class outfitted for the most discriminating patrons. At the helm was seasoned Captain Edward Smith, secretly intent on pleasing an important passenger, Mr. Bruce Ismay, chairman of the White Star Lines, with a new record time for crossing the Atlantic.

The captain, confident and careless, perhaps unused to a ship of this new size, ignored or downplayed the significance of reports of ice floes and bergs ahead. He and his ship were invincible. There would be no ice in his shipping lane, no need to slow down. At the end of the voyage would be kudos for him and profit for the White Star Lines — a company which had office space in Spencer's Manhattan building.

Among the *Titanic's* passengers in first class quarters on the upper deck were the John Jacob Astors from New York, returning home to the States with lady's maid, a private nurse (the very young second Mrs. Astor was pregnant) and their little dog.[126] Also enjoying the *Titanic's* evenings of fine dining, dancing, and opulent entertainment were the wealthy Jewish businessman Benjamin Guggenheim; Mr. and Mrs. Isidor Straus who with a brother owned Macy's; an aide to President Taft; and numerous millionaire families. The passenger list of course also included the working-class passengers, mostly "unknowns" in third-class quarters, passengers well below the first-class deck where a chain across the stairs reminded all of the separation along class lines. Class lines were well delineated, but the calamity would be shared by all before the night was over.

At 11:40 on Sunday night the Titanic's starboard side scored the looming iceberg, and a 300-foot-long gaping slash opened the chambers below to the icy Atlantic waters. The behemoth ship listed forward into the bow as the chambers filled. A startled captain ordered the 16 lifeboats filled, life boats with capacity for only half the number of human beings on the ship. "Women and children first" were the orders, and Mr. Astor calmly had seen his young wife placed with her maid in the last raft, bidding her "good bye 'til the morning."[127]

How ghostly it must have been for the shivering women in the life boats watching the obscene tilt of the *Titanic* still ablaze with lights, knowing there would be no morning for those silhouetted figures seen clinging to the rails as the water now washed over the upper deck. A few hours later, in a cacophony of breaking china, splintering wood, cracking smokestacks, sucking water, and terrified cries of passengers left on board, the great hulk disappeared beneath the water, leaving an eerie silence punctuated by faint cries here and there in the black waters. Days later the passenger lists of survivors were released: there were 705 who lived; 705 out of 2,226 passengers and crew.

We here at Yaddo were to learn that someone in our "family" had suffered a grievous loss. One of our Yaddo kitchen maids Maevis O'Brien had lost her brother and his wife and children, and a sister with two little girls that night; this family had left a tiny town in Ireland to find opportunities in the factories of New York, and had almost reached their promised land. Maevis had arranged their journey to Troy and jobs at the Cluett, Peabody and Company collar factory. I spent many days in April consoling a badly shaken Maevis and trying to share with her my Faith's verses and my own methods for dealing with pain and loss.

Her family's lost ones were never recovered from the ocean, but we learned that John Jacob Astor's body had finally been located ten days later, bloated and disfigured, floating near Newfoundland, his gold watch still in his pocket, a diamond ring still on his finger, a large roll of British pounds in his wallet, golf cufflinks set with diamonds still holding the wrists of his shirt. We read that his pregnant wife Madeleine had been sent to safety in lifeboat four, along with her maids, and that she had protected and hidden a man on their lifeboat who had disguised himself as a woman in his panic for safety.[128]

The *Titanic* story was a major event in 1912, along with a shocking and divisive presidential election, and at Yaddo there was a feeling that we were at a watershed time in history, with the Unknown in the shadows before us. It was an unsettling time for the whole family at Yaddo, and for all Americans living in "the Gilded Age." It was hard to continue to be optimistic, believing in the ever Onward and Upward march of our progressive age. Perhaps the times of Plenty and Peace were about to end. We were sailing in precarious waters.

And besides his fervent "duty" to Mrs. Trask, what work of the world called forth Mr. Peabody during these years "after Spencer"? By 1906 he had retired from the business world, had left Spencer Trask and Company at aged fifty-four, primarily to work with his many philanthropies. He was a multi-millionaire — though not in the category of the Astors, Carnegies, Vanderbilts, Rockefellers, and Morgans — a wealthy and generous man of high morals who took pleasure in entertaining his friends, and putting people together for philanthropic causes. He continued his support of the Episcopal Church and enjoyed the close friendship of Reverend Mellish in New York city's Trinity Church and Bishop Doane in Albany. He supported countless educational institutes in the south and in Colorado and invested on Wall Street the funds entrusted to him by many boards and institutions. He was a great supporter of the University of Georgia and I had the pleasure of helping with this endeavor once.

The college needed a tiled pool, he said; and estimating the cost at around $3,000, I opened his hand and placed in it the sapphire ring from my finger. *I think the school needs a pool, and you need to sell my ring and give it to them,* I had suggested.[129] His arms encircled me for a long time. Mind you, it was not "the widow's mite" I was offering. There were many Italian gold rings and brilliant gems from Venice in my velvet box, but he was deeply moved.

When Spencer died, Foster was named an executor of the estate, along with me and my brother Acosta

Nichols. He immediately took over Spencer's responsi-
bilities on the Saratoga Springs Commission and took a
house at number nineteen Circular Street in Saratoga
where he set up his "headquarters,"[130] not wanting to
"overstay" his open invitation and designated suite at
Yaddo. He continued the detailed study of making Saratoga Springs a health spa once again, and recommended
to the governor the purchase of certain land parcels near
the exhausted ones to acquire the potential minerals for
the iconic Saratoga spring water.

Foster also became deeply involved in the Wilson
Administration beginning in 1912 and corresponded
closely with the President, inviting him and his wife to
Abenia, offering opinions and suggestions in requested
literary dialogue. Foster turned down the President's
offer of Secretary of the Treasury because he felt he
could "render my largest quota of public service outside
the constraints of office."[131] He would be very active in
the New York Federal Reserve Bank recently set up by
the Federal Reserve Act and he worked hard to encourage public trust in the new system as well as to assist in
the floating of war loans and bond issues by 1917 when
we entered the War.

Foster supported regulating of monopoly and
wanted the government to control public utilities, and
so was happy to see progressive regulation such as the
Clayton Act and the setting up of the Federal Trade
Commission come to be law.[132] In 1917 he joined the
board of the new Skidmore College founded by Lucy
Scribner back in 1903 for practical training for women.

Foster Peabody was a staunch supporter of women's causes, and believed they should have the right to vote. We had many a debate on this last issue, as I had not yet decided to join the cause: there were other more pressing issues for women. There was an inner growth, an intellectual and spiritual power which women needed to seize upon and direct their energies towards before taking on the sober responsibility of the franchise. Other influential women were fiercely working for suffrage, women like Alva Vanderbilt Belmont in Newport, but for me it was not woman's greatest priority.

But Foster's greatest cause was that of neutrality in the coming war, and he worked tirelessly on the cause of peace. He wrote pieces for magazines, letters to Congressmen and the President, and of course he was the greatest supporter of my book *In the Vanguard* which he mailed out to people all over the country. He felt my book had a great impact on keeping America out of the war earlier, a book which he felt "was a real factor in developing the sentiment which was back of President Wilson's delay in entering the war."[133]

It is known that the German atrocities between 1914 and 1917 against American ships became so egregious that neutrality and non-intervention were no longer viable alternatives to fighting. Still I battled with the pen, writing *The Conquering Army*, another play for the cause of peace. But in 1916, Foster and I both supported President Wilson's re-election campaign, with its campaign slogan "he kept us out of war." When the Declaration of War finally came on April 6, 1917, Foster and I both wanted to state publicly that though our views on pacifism had not changed, we would abide by the law, support the President and the war efforts, and encourage the buying of war bonds.[134]

After Spencer's death, the Saratoga Springs town fathers had wanted to honor him for his work for the town, and they decided to commission a memorial sculpture to be placed in beautiful Congress Park. The town (with my input after Foster's inspired suggestion) hired the renowned sculptor Daniel Chester French in nearby Stockbridge to create *The Spirit of Life* statue, but it came into being as a happy result of an ugly process I detested, a lawsuit. I had been against it, suing the New York Central Railroad after the tragic accident, but it had to be done, according to my advisers and my attorney brother. The railroads must be held accountable to the public. It was for the greater good.

When the insurance money came, I gifted it to the Town of Saratoga Springs, but I did not want to seem overly directive as to its use. At the same time, I had ideas as to "appropriateness" and artistic "integrity" and Spencer had enjoyed a fine relationship with Daniel French through his art societies and popular studio soirees. Together the town fathers and I agreed on a concept for a statue and I directed them to Daniel French, whom Foster and Spencer respected greatly.

Daniel Chester French's Greenwich Village atelier was often filled with the social elite of New York and

America's finest sculptors, and Spencer had been to a number of his studio parties. DC had won acclaim for producing the largest sculpture in America, his *Republic* which stood in gold-leaf glory out in Chicago at the World's Columbian Exhibition back in 1892. Spencer and I had traveled to the Exhibition along with many Americans from all walks of life and we had stood in amazement at the statue in the Court of Honor, almost as grand as the new French statue — *Liberty Enlightening the World* — in New York harbor.[135] Modeled on young New York socialite Edith Minturn, French's imposing female figure of sixty-five feet on a thirty-foot pedestal represented the symbolic patriotic and proud America. I was relieved when the Town contract with French was signed, and pleased to entrust my husband's tribute statue to such a talent.

Since I was indisposed, Foster acted as family representative during the time of the work. How I wanted to accompany Foster to Chesterwood that summer as the work progressed, but I trusted his exquisite artistic judgment and waited with great anticipation for his returns from the Berkshires as he relayed the progress. Evidently, the piece in progress often was brought out into natural light from the Chesterwood studio on rails which extended from the studio barn to several feet outside into the lawn. Foster reported on the development of the statue with pleasure, but at one point I had to intervene... I wanted an active pose for the statue, a statue which was energized and life-giving, and so we started over with these instructions.

My apologies went to DC, but we understood each

other, in fact we shared other areas of common interest and support. We were great supporters of institutes for the blind and deaf, and I so admired his memorial work for Gallaudet University for the deaf, the magnificent bronze statue of the seated teacher with his standing deaf pupil Alice Cogswell receiving his "handspeak" with a stick on her open palm. I wrote to him after Foster came home with his final report of the progress:

"All hail, O Master Sculptor... I thought because of my personal connection I would be coldly analytical and critical, and yet it works the other way. I think it is the best thing you have ever done and agree with others who know your place in the Temple of Fame."[136]

The *Spirit of Life* bronze was beautifully completed to my liking, the classical female figure with her voluminous robes and outstretched hands holding a pine branch, Spencer's "emblem," and a bowl of life-giving Saratoga water, nourishment offered to those who gaze upon her lovely form. Spencer would have loved this tribute statue, done with "nine-tenths mechanical work, one-tenth poet," as DC once said. It was the creation of the genius who was simultaneously hard at work creating his masterpiece, the statue of the seated Lincoln, which would be enshrined in its classical temple in the nation's capital some years later.

It was another morning of poring over all my daily newspapers on the chaise. Piles of papers, and my stubby pen and silver magnifying glass. The staff had come to recognize "Katrina's conversations with herself," my quite loud conversations with the various headlines and articles. Sometimes I shouted to the ceiling. This day my maid was readying the bath for me and came running back into my room. Did I call her?

"No, Mary, just another loud protest from this invalid lady here. Mary, I ask you now, why is it a man should be loudly praised because he is willing to die for his principles in War, and yet be called a coward when he is willing to die for his principles of Peace? Really, does it MAKE SENSE to you? How proud I am of our President for keeping us out of war. His address last night was the most statesmanlike address in American history! Oh Mary, words FAIL before the horror of war."

"Shall I hold the bathwater, my lady?"

It was hopeless. War, I knew, WOULD come to our country, and soon.

I already had begun to think of closing down the big house and moving out to a smaller farmhouse on the property. Finances were tight, fuel dear, and Yaddo's future was at stake if the money dried up. I would so miss this wonderful room with its expansive views, my window personally inscribed with the "double kingdom" poem by Henry van Dyke... *For Katrina's Window...* the window pane "separating the Kingdom of Nature from the Kingdom of Love inside." How lovely a sentiment in those words running the length of my broad window. And how ugly the world was about to become.

These were anxious conflicted days of questioning for America, with secret support for the Allies, but no war declared. I labored for peace with my pen, articles here and there, letters to Congress and to Mr. Wilson. My book *In The Vanguard* had been read aloud all over the country and had been done "in point" for the blind. How this pleased me, as I had been facing the possibility of total blindness all winter. I corresponded regularly with Elisabeth, my cherished Queen of Rumania and author of many essays and poems and folk tales from her country, but we could not discuss my pacifism because she was in the "heart of warmongering countries" and had to defend her country. Our souls were of one in so many aspects: the loss of our daughters; the dimming of our eyesight; the Red Cross causes we both supported; our philosophical ideas of government, with the favoring of a republic over a monarchy... and *she* the monarch of her country.

My poems and hers could be from the same heart and written in the same style. I told her of my cottage here by the lake, of my book for the blind, and tried to cheer her in her own work for the blind there. I told her I was having her *Fairy Tales* translated into English, and urged her to leave court and go to the quiet country to find solace. She still painfully grieved for her lost daughter, a special child brought down by scarlet fever and entombed in her palace garden. The queen was an acclaimed poet and a philosopher, that was known, but she was active and practical in her life, as well. Elisabeth was a doer. She was a great champion for the blind in her small country, having set up communes for practical training of the blind and the deaf in a country where many physically *un*encumbered people were still illiterate. She was trying to finance individual printing machines or typewriters for self-expression in her communes. She was battling to open doors for the unfortunate souls forever imprisoned in their infirmities which denied them sight and sound.

Some years ago she had written to me of a special friend of hers who was coming to America, someone who was coming to discuss international peace. He was Archbishop Germanos of the Greek Church from Baalbek, Syria, and she felt "the romance and symbolism and poetry of that church would appeal to my nature."[137] In 1915 I had entertained him at Yaddo, my last official guest, this strange man from the Middle East; now I invited him back, not to the boarded doors of the big house, but to my new little farmhouse, with its simple lines and its lovely outlook.

As I explained, there I could offer hospitality but no money. Through an interpreter, we communicated: our hearts were perfectly in tune that day. I had heard he was like Isaiah and was near to God and could see the future. He asked about my life in this new place, how it would be. He knelt on the ground, facing the little farmhouse's new wing being constructed, and then after a long silence he made the sign of the cross and rose. Hajjar his interpreter spoke to me then:

"His Eminence says a great blessing shall rest upon the house. You will see the fruit of all your labors and you will do greater work there than you have yet done. Henceforth this house shall be called The House of Happiness."[138]

In Arabic, the name was *Mansel Alsaada*. I do believe that strange message from the Eternal through this Arab man was meant to find a poor soul like me. It was meant as a sign for me to go on, calmly close my beautiful house and cheerfully make this new home all it was meant to be. A "gate" was opened for me that day when he came to the new location, and by this quiet dark man from the other side of the world. It was the beginning of a lovely friendship, an important friendship, and he came again in 1918, this time walking to the highest point of Yaddo where he said he found a sense of peace, a mystic presence. He and I walked "reverently" over the entire hillside, and I also felt a peace I had not felt anywhere else at Yaddo. He walked with me to a beautiful clearing surrounded by pines, a place where Foster and I had loved one another with great passion, a place with the most heavenly views in all directions. Through the interpreter, the Bishop named the place for me. "It shall be called Holy Hill." He promised to send me a stone from Jerusalem to mark the place where I would come to rest one day.

This high place he christened *Tel-Almukaddas* and I knew it would be my final resting place on earth.

And I decided at that moment that my "circle of friends" would also rest there beside me, my heart's dearest Foster Peabody and my sister–friend Allena Pardee. And there should be a stone marking the spirit of my husband Spencer Trask. His spirituality, compassion for his fellow man, and zest for living purposefully I had taken as my own design for living. Spencer would always be with me.

On the political front at home, I confess I had lost my abject hero worship for President Wilson, but I was pleased we were saved from the "reactionary conservatism and the dark-age policies of the Republicans."[139] The election of 1912 had found the Republican party supporting the reactionary Taft, but divided by the newly-formed Bull Moose Party of Theodore Roosevelt. The Democrats had won the election, bringing to the White House the intellectual, progressive, and reform-minded Woodrow Wilson. Much legislative progress had been achieved under Mr. Wilson in the realm of social reforms. Child labor laws were enacted and railroad workers were protected from long and grueling work days. A new piece of legislation regulated the banks and set up the Federal Reserve System to watch over national credit and the money supply. A federal income tax was passed. I wondered how this historic move would affect the charitable work of the wealthy, how it would affect my own life. Time would tell. Our President had worked hard to keep us out of the war which was flaring across the Atlantic in the summer of 1914. He and Foster were in contact constantly, though unofficially: the President knew he was a "wise counselor."

The following year the sinking of the British ocean liner *Lusitania* by a German torpedo provided the spark for our President to "issue a warning" to the Germans. Still our country resisted a war declaration, and still we "unofficially" aided our British friends. One hundred twenty-eight Americans were dead in that *Lusitania* tragedy, yet still I prayed for peace and for continued neutrality. If ultimately we were *forced* to join the war, *then* I would support it wholeheartedly: the sooner we could defeat the barbarism of the Germans, the sooner would come peace for all. I already had prepared my self and my household for the exigencies of war by closing down the big house in 1916 and moving to the smaller farmhouse. This I did with heavy heart, after the *Lusitania,* knowing perhaps the ultimate inevitability of our country's war declaration. Finally, when the *Times* announced our country's entry into World War I in April of 1917 I sent a Western Union telegram to Adolph Ochs there, a man for whom I had a great personal affection:

"My deepest congratulations and my heartfelt sympathy with the dignified and satisfactory course of the Times *in this unspeakable crisis. You know my strong feeling for Peace... but Germany has left us no choice and it is our moral duty to make a firm and active protest against such unspeakable high-handedness."*

With our entry into the war, I dedicated Yaddo to the war effort on the home front. We put the fields of Yaddo to work for the country. More belt-tightening would occur, but flags adorned the lawns of Yaddo, the household hoed and planted, preserved, and canned. I invited citizens of Saratoga to farm our land for the war effort. Sheep were raised here at Yaddo for the wool for combat uniforms. At first I had written this question:

"In this vortex of horror what right has any one to plan for beauty? In this awful suffering what justification is there for any one to dwell on the thought of an intellec-

tual retreat? Art seems as far off, as unimportant and as unthinkable as does a study of the flora in the midst of the deluge. But slowly, during this long bitter year, the thought has been growing that perhaps it is more important to work for the preservation of beauty…" [140]

So I never forgot the great dream for Yaddo: I simply put it aside to confront the war dragon.

With the country's entry into the fray, Foster and I both now would be working hard to muster national support for the buying of war bonds. American troops were massing on ships' piers, factories boomed with activity as more devastating pictures and reports came from Europe. Flags waved fiercely in the hands of small children, but behind them stood mothers with fear in their eyes. Newspapers daily exposed the barbarism of the Germans. Eyes turned away from images of the slaughtered in mud-filled trenches, the horrid gassing of young manhood. Although we were protected here in the quiet of up-state New York, though we were spared the new and strange sounds of tanks and automatic weapons, we sensed an awful truth. We were in the midst of a great blood-letting in the world like we had never dreamed possible.

I allowed myself, then, some large *DECISIONS* and raised some frightening QUESTIONS.

First, since American men were away fighting a war, then the country should at last *allow women the right to vote*. I was making a leap into a cause I had put aside as "too early," too "ill-advised." Now I joined the Woman Suffrage party and contributed to my own state's New York State Woman Suffrage Party. This was a big step for me, and a surprising one for those who knew me. Long had this been an issue in our country, raised seriously after the Civil War, when Negroes were given the vote through a constitutional amendment. Truthfully, my lack of a voting right had never much troubled me. My view held that women were endowed with unique powers and that it was important for women to spend their energies developing these powers to guide and influence men to act nobly and choose paths of benevolence in their dealings with others. Women were the great force behind men in their actions for the common good. I had not joined any of the various suffrage movements, many of which I found distasteful and unproductive in their *methods* of proselytizing for women's right to vote.

But that was not the real reason for my earlier lack of support of the suffragettes. The Party thought the spiritual emancipation of women could be developed better after suffrage was granted; I believed the *"political freedom would be a danger, rather than a good, until women had first gained their needed spiritual emancipation and had become possessed of the winged freedom of their own souls."*[141] Women working so fervently for the vote were wasting their great energy on a lesser cause instead of giving their zeal to the study of woman's supreme mission, WOMANHOOD.

Women had not claimed the great divine power given to them not just for bearing children, but for making their own selves and their homes a loftier place, a stimulating place, an educated and morally steadfast place. It was an ideal, but it seemed to me a practical path. Until now. Now all is changed. How can I go on "hugging my ideals" when the ground is rocking with war? Practicality has intervened. It is a *practical necessity* for women to be able to vote and take the helm of the ship of State in the absence of the country's male population. We women are beset with new and unprecedented duties and the franchise will give us a sense of partnership with our government. Women must rely on themselves, make decisions, work with their hands and their hearts and their minds to do unprecedented chores. Women must become the new leaders in this extraordinary situation.

"*Nothing ever develops character and calls forth true wisdom as does responsibility,*" I wrote. "*It is of the utmost consequence, therefore, that this year 1917 shall signalize the advance of New York state by granting women their inherent right to say their full conviction as to government by having equal voting rights with the men.*"

And so I wrote in *The Woman Citizen*[142] which was reprinted in the *Times*. It would be later, in 1920, when the nineteenth amendment to the Constitution granted women the right to vote. But in the meantime, New York state joined others in offering the suffrage to women in 1917. President Wilson changed his position on the issue, and I wondered what influence Foster's persuasive words and writings had in this matter. To those women who worked undaunted from the time of the Civil War to the present for this achievement, I give supreme credit in this crusade.

And what if the Allied Powers were unsuccessful in obtaining this Wilsonian "new freedom" for the world? What if we could not "make the world safe for democracy"? What if the war went on and on, and the German order of "might makes right" prevailed? God help us, then all hopes would be dashed for a new order of justice and a reign of creativity to uplift the hearts of Man. There would be no place for a Yaddo. Or for Katrina Trask. We in America would have to live with this frightening question for over a year, all the while keeping hands working and hearts full of hope in the power of good over evil. This MUST be the war to end all wars. ❧

"The Spirit of Life" tribute statue to
Spencer Trask, 1914, by Daniel Chester French.
Located in Congress Park, Saratoga Springs.
{ Photo by the author }

Chapter Seven

House of Happiness

"Ring out wild bells to the wild sky!" Let the chimes ring over the whole earth, for this war is ended. Months ago the barbarians were stopped and freedom has triumphed. But at what price, with ten million men dead and hundred of thousands wounded and maimed. Two empires have toppled in Europe, the Ottoman and the Hapsburg, and the Russian empire seems threatened with revolution at home. Our country has just ended its first foray into world affairs, but our war was not the heroic idyll we expected. The map of the world is different, new national lines have encircled strange ethnic bedfellows where the old empires reigned, and it will be a challenge to keep the peace so dearly won.

Peace, now, will reign if only the people will support Mr. Wilson's League of Nations and the idea of dialogue, not destruction. If only all the nations would embrace ideas of respect and co-existence and spend their coffers on helping their people and raising their aspirations for a bountiful life, both materially and spiritually. Our soldiers are home hopefully to embrace a courageous new world. I am alive with thankfulness and with great expectations for our nation, refusing to think we could shirk our duties as part of the world effort to maintain peace. Last night I wrote a poem on peace in the midst of my exalted mood and saved it in my head for Allena's typewriter tomorrow.

I must confess that I have not always been so full of hope and cheer over the past year-and-a-half. Despair and desolation are not in my acceptable vocabulary of emotions, and I have done brave personal battle against these demons. My doctors NOW offer no hope of improvement of my vision and my general heart health. The hemorrhages, the days of bandages over the eyes, the fatigue and weakness in the limbs... they have dogged my days while this war raged on overseas. If the doctors had *said* death I would have died "in harness" still writing until the end. But blindness? Not to see color and dappled light? Never to gaze from my window to endless horizons of mountains to the east? Never to pen my little rhymes for downstairs dinner guests in calligraphy? Oh, my Jesus, *death*, not blindness, I have implored. And so, through a merciful God, for now, I am spared total blindness but am confined to my horizontal position on this chaise, ever dependent on Allena and her typewriter.

How often over the next several years I began my correspondence with apologies for the sheer *coldness* of this typing machine. I work to have the warmth of my heart shine through. Yes, still the typewritten words go out, imploring, objecting, agreeing, encouraging, but always "going out." Still I ask the reviewers to be objective, not servile, in their comments on my poems or stories: I want to *learn* from their negative remarks or comments. My eyesight is so weak and I mourn for the days when I saw subtle color in a rose and did not miss the single bud in the bouquet; but my sense of smell and touch are *much* strengthened and I delight in the perfume of my roses, the fuzzy feel at the center of a black-eyed Susan, the linear structure of the field lupine. Helen, my dear Miss Keller, you made this all possible for me, just as I helped you with my works in point. Something is taken away, something is given.

Foster has been working hard to grow my funds, funds surprisingly small, and he himself has sold Abenia and moved to Circular Street in Saratoga in an effort to conserve his own money and work on some of his Saratoga projects. Happily he found the perfect buyer for Abenia in our friend Adolph Ochs who now has his own piece of paradise at Lake George. I understand he and Mr. Bixby have become great friends and share many interests.

And now, my reader, I bring to you my Great Secret, which I wrote first to Adolph Ochs at the *Times* on a bright cold day in January of 1921. I kept it in my heart for many months and repeated it aloud in my room only just before Allena came to me with her typewriter. I would tell Adolph the secret and next week I would tell my most intimate friends so they would know before it was announced in the paper. The secret read like this:

"On the fifth day of February next I am to be married to Foster Peabody, thus consummating and crowning a romance and poem of love more perfect and more beautiful than any which has ever been written. For forty years

Foster has given to me a most beautiful devotion. The chivalrous love of the troubadours, which always interested me so much, seems as nothing compared to the infinite splendor that has been flashed upon my life.

"I said I was too old. 'No, you are simply immortal and you are becoming conscious of your immortality.' I am a confirmed invalid. 'Well, if you are, you but give me the greater opportunity for service which is what I desire.' What use to argue against such chivalrous logic. And so I ceased arguing and gave myself to him feeling that no one would be more pleased at my decision than Spencer.

"A great happiness has come into my life. In spite of an illness, serious and mortal, in spite of age and in spite of the burden of sorrows, a great happiness and fresh young joy fill my days and nights... a new star has arisen with promise and prophecy."[143]

I knew Adolph would be somewhat surprised, knowing I had refused marriage for a long time. I went on to describe how Foster had stood aside "in reverent silence while I was vibrating from the shock of Spencer's death."[144] Time passed, new sorrows came, and Foster taught me "how to die and how to live... he gave me daily bread of a triune nature... material, spiritual, mental." Our love grew like a beautiful morning surprised by the mystery of its beginning. He implored me to marry him and refused to listen to my arguments against the proposal.

"I was, AM, dying, dying here at Yaddo,"
I insisted.

"Well, if you are, it is the kind of dying we are ordered to accomplish... the daily dying of the seed to

bring forth the perfect fruit."[145]

There it was, the argument so beautifully constructed, begun again. Was that argument now stronger, or was I weaker? If the latter, how sweet is weakness.

Later, I sent a congratulatory note to Adolph for the delicate and gracious way the paper had handled the announcement.

"Foster and I are intertwined in a most wonderful way... closely bound by spiritual as well as earthly ties. It seemed to me that the marriage could never be because I was so ill and still am so very ill, but I KNOW NOW THAT IT COULD NOT NOT BE. It was ordained by God and brings eternal beauty."[146]

And, because I am Woman, and vain, I thanked him for using an earlier photograph of me before illness and sorrow had left their tracks upon my face. Foster's photograph showed his beautiful visage, still so handsome and strong. Yes, I was very, very happy in February. Did I sense it might be the last February of my life? February that was my daughter's favorite winter month in the city. February that saw my second wedding day.

Our ceremony on that winter's day was a quiet one, held in my little House of Happiness with only the minister and his wife Mrs. Edwin Knox Mitchell of Hartford, Connecticut, my niece most beloved to me, and of course Allena and the household staff. I smiled later at the column "Tea Table Chat" in the Saratoga newspaper which carried a description of the Rose Room where we exchanged our vows... the room with "rose carpet, rose velour divans, and rose-tinted walls"[147] and the lady "in white silken Grecian robes, for the Lady of Yaddo never wears woman's usual garb." The lady always "seemed the heart of the rose," they noted, "giving of her heart, mind, and soul to the outside world." I had put down the papers, dozens of them announcing our marriage, and closed my eyes, contentedly. Other people were celebrating our personal happiness. The most gratifying comment to me, however, was that welcoming note to my new husband:

"*Congratulations, our beloved lady, and welcome, Host of Yaddo.*"

At last Foster officially and legitimately could claim the position he had nobly held for so many years at my side. The *Saratoga Sun* noted that "it is impossible to name two persons who have done more to maintain the prestige and advance the welfare of this famous city and resort than have Mr. and Mrs. Peabody."[148] And further: "The ladies of the household wore soft voile dresses, a gift from Mrs. Trask, matching Katrina's simple white satin gown, and the mantle of snow lay over all of Yaddo." It was dramatic and too detailed, but I suppose people were curious. The paper described the beautiful twin white brooches, the "quite rare gems," which "the groom had bestowed upon the bride." The *New York Times* announced, as I had told Adolph, that our marriage was "a happy culmination of a lifelong friendship in which romance and chivalry have had a large part."[149] It stated that Mr. Peabody was sixty-nine, Mrs. Peabody sixty-eight. To us the ages mattered not at all: the sparks had endured and the old flames glowed quietly.

On the Monday after our wedding, Foster

announced that he would give his residence at number ninteen Circular Street "for the welfare of the women of Saratoga Springs."[150] He named it for me, the Katrina Trask Hall, and gave it this motto:

"If we love not the human soul we have seen, how can we love God, whom we have not seen?"[151]

The dedication of the house, similar to that of Wiawaka's dedication, was in "recognition of and with reverent gratitude for THE WOMAN SOUL, ever leading onward and upward" and he gave this home in honor of his bride so that various social and religious work in Saratoga could occur in one place. My great goal was here enshrined, my goal that "women should recognize the great power within themselves, different from men, a psychological endowment given women, a divine Possibility"[152] which could be cultivated and used to transform the world.

How many notes of congratulations we did receive over the next few days, some from London, Paris, New York, a ship in the Pacific... and our House of Happiness became a bower of bouquets and flower arrangements. There was a gift and note from the White House with personal blessings for our marriage. So much love bestowed on Foster and me to begin our married life together, even if to the outside world our journey seemed begun very, very late. Perhaps of late I was beginning to feel my mortality, and to think of the other life, but on that winter wedding day nothing mattered but being in the light of my love and feeling the strength of his hand in mine as we mouthed the words we had already claimed as ours a lifetime ago. Foster had been a gift from above, to Spencer and to me, and there was no part of Yaddo that he had not shaped, no corner that knew not his touch artistically, no part of the spiritual life of the house which escaped the *"splendour of his spacious soul."*[153] Yaddo was his as much as mine, and it belonged to him as it had to Spencer. The three of us were intertwined in the fabric of the estate and in its destiny, and in the end, one of us would be left to nurture it until its time of delivery to the world of art. I always knew, of course, that that one would be Foster Peabody. I had chosen well.

And so almost a year passed, a blissful year of happiness in my marriage, but a difficult year of physical suffering... the chest pains, the weakness, the gradual dimming of light in my only eye with vision, the persistent and strangely irresistible feeling of drifting away, quietly, with the end of the year, into a lovely beckoning snow storm. We had enjoyed "a picnic day" in the summer on the east grounds of Yaddo, where I could view the garden and gaze up at my tower room. Then it was mostly pillows and down comforters, the smell of roses by the bed, Foster's warm hand clasping mine. There were frequent beautiful staccato moments of music being played somewhere, of poetry read to me in Foster's quiet voice, of Allena's cheerful relaying of messages from friends, of kindly doctors bending over me with too-bright voices of encouragement, of Foster's tired head drooping now in the bedside chair, still holding my hand until sleep came... those windy evenings with a shutter flapping... and so often, now, I confuse the present with the past.

It is January of 1922 .... Or is it still the war years?
... horrid years which coaxed out my brave polemics
against war.

Why must brave men for ever go,
And be forever slain?
Then, sudden, in the shadows dim,
Alive, aflame, afar
Upon the dark horizon's rim,
Behold a Morning Star.

Prophetic Star of Brotherhood
Herald of War's surcease:
A Star of everlasting good,
An Advent Star of Peace.

By that clear light I can foresee
Upon the travailing earth,
New life for all humanity,
New Freedom, and new birth.

Lo! when reborn, victorious,
We stand with blossoming Rod.
Then shall we know the glorious
Wherefore and Why of God.[154]

There now, I shall send this peace poem to the Ochs
this Thanksgiving, but first I must read it to Spencer.
My darling will be so pleased that I am writing again. I
am making a verse, a humorous rhyme, to send down to
the dining room... with apologies to my guests.

Christina keeps her brush pens in the ivory elephant box, and she will be delighted that I have used her favorite blue one. Doctor says I must stay in bed and not come down to greet my guests; perhaps they can come, one by one, to my sitting room so that I might be warm and inviting to those who come so far for dinner at Yaddo. I do so long to see Lord Kelvin. I want to hear the story of the cable again, the laying of the cable on the Atlantic floor. We simply MUST entertain him before he returns to England. Allena, please bring your horrid little machine and take my letter, my letter, take my letter to… Elisabeth. How she suffers, a sad queen so far away. Her little daughter lost in white satin and lace, laid cold as marble in the palace garden tomb.

My garden is a gift of love. I intend to open it to all who would enjoy its beauty. I will stress this point tomorrow in the interview with the editor of the *Country Calendar*. My rose garden will not be "a statistical place which is entered with notebooks, to compare the relative size and allure of the many varieties."[155] No botanical names in gardens and wild places here, just happy names of happy flowers. And Allena, take this down:

"He who gazes at our sun-dial and its message, and he who gathers roses from our garden will take pause and remember the futility of the things of time, and the immortality of the spirit, which is Love, and will come up from our garden a wiser man."[156]

That in writing, Allena, please.

Roses in the front parlor, Allena, and the guest list for tonight. We have the best conversations when we are twelve. Roses on the table in the Tiffany vases. Wildflowers in the library, please. All yellow. An affirmative color. The St. Christina girls, and the little ones at Wiawaka. Our special wildflowers Spencer always said. Roses. Foster's roses twining about the deck of the *Pocahontas*, and Spencer's roses, row after row, after row... I shall make the rose my emblem.

The afternoon tea party at Arthur de Ferraris' studio: Arthur, YOU must be the one to paint our portraits. We invite you next season to Yaddo. You will then see the portraits hanging in the Great Hall. Is that a promise, Arthur? Our portraits? Please, you must do Spencer first, standing, I should think, showing calm, control, the chin set just right... and dressed in period costume of an English squire. And I in simple white, of course... perhaps with roses in my arms?

Spencer. How dedicated you are. Your bent head in your books, tallying numbers, and sometimes sketching in the margins, always working. The consummate fundraiser... the hospital, the Art Society, the Armenians, now the restoration of Venice's campanile, its bell tower that collapsed.

Venice, jewel-like, floating in ruined splendor. Oh, Spencer, do you remember? The palazzo Rezzonico where Elizabeth and Robert Browning stayed? My favorite place, Venice. Venezia… a gem among cities. We should bring the Brustolon carved armchairs up from Tuxedo Park. The Tuxedo house is gone. Sold. 1916, I believe. The Brooklyn house, Gramercy Park, I can't recall where we were… Spencer, we shall build our own Venice here, here in this paradise on the lake, the lake…

The eye. I see the eye, the dreadful sight of the eye in the dish by the bedside, the beautiful face spilling blood into the basin… oh, my poor brave Spencer. Not his beautiful eye. And my ONE eye… cloudy and dim; oh, to tear it from my face and die with Spencer on the Croton tracks.

Flowers and a photograph from the President. Foster, do you see how much they love you? You must write the Wilsons. Invite them to Yaddo so he might find strength to fight his illness. We shall open the big house permanently, not just for a picnic. Should we add a downstairs bath? And what to do about the ceiling leaks? In my desk, the list of all the paint samples for the downstairs rooms. Do fetch the paint samples. It must be done properly. Allena knows. Find Allena.

Christina is a gifted child, you know. Such wisdom for her years. How can she know Truths at eight and nine when older people profess to have the wisdom of the ages? She but smiles as Junius invades her desk, her books and treasures with his sunny impish pranks.

How she bears his constant naughtiness, and "checks the hasty word, and gives the gentle answer back"! Our Christina is a supreme Celebrant of Life. There she is, jumping in the barn, swinging from the rafters, oh, take care, and no, don't coax your pony so. Too fast, my love. On her pony, untied chestnut hair flying behind her, wild peals of laughter, head thrown back to love the sky, the speed, the apple tree blurred in passing.

She WILL not write in her book in summer. Too much life to celebrate. She will write and work and study in winter, curled up with grey shawl in her bay window with notebook and Bible and favorite verses. A child of summer, yet will she use the winter wisely. February, her favorite winter month. A lap full of drawing pens and paper Valentines, frilly white edges, cutouts of bluebirds, pressed summer flowers still bright on the crimson bits of felt. She will come to me on winter evenings in the city, come softly to my bed with hugs and love spilling over and some serious topics which she has been mulling over in her head. And we will talk of things seen and unseen. She is a child unafraid of dark things in the night, because she sees the poet's morning star. *"Don't you just LOVE Longfellow, Mama? I think he has the longest white beard."*[157]

I think it is your white hair that is my favorite thing about you, darling. I love the way it covers your face early in the morning, all askew and un-composed.

Waiting for your perfect toilette, your putting perfect, reasonable order on all things. You have the perfect visage and you have the perfect words. You are the perfect circle. How do I deserve you, Foster? What did I do that was SO RIGHT?

I believe it is January. Today I feel the snow. It is so cold, but I know they are all here, my household of Yaddo, all of them, my circle of friends, Allena and Foster. We are moving steeply upward, along a curving path, and they are clearing the way as we pass the Stone Tower. With strong evergreen boughs they are sweeping away the masses of snowflakes to clear the ground so they may bear their burden more easily all the way to *Tel-Almukaddas*. The view from there is beautiful. I can see far away very clearly, and it is beautiful. ❀

George Foster Peabody at Yaddo on the
occasion of his 80th birthday in 1932.
He survived Katrina by sixteen years, dying in 1938.
{ Courtesy Saratoga Springs History Museum }

Photo of Yaddo mansion designed after the
English manor house Haddon Hall, built on site of
the original Queen Anne-style house which burned
in 1891. Construction completed in 1893.

{ Courtesy Saratoga Springs History Museum }

The Legacy of Yaddo

Katrina Trask died on January 8, 1922, and was buried on the highest hill of her estate, Yaddo, in the midst of a blinding snowstorm. Her "frail hand and woman's heart" had initiated forces that she hoped would come to influence the world for the better. The *Troy Record* that week dramatically reported her burial: "Nature's funeral dirge, a strong wind blowing, sang for one who loved Nature and its beauty." The lower path leading to *Tel Almukaddos* had been swept clear of the snow, and the higher areas were covered with pine boughs to make easier the pathway to the burial site .

She had lived as an invalid for almost ten years on the grounds of Yaddo and was surrounded by those who loved her. Perhaps it was too soon to die, as was the case with Princess Diana in that Parisian tunnel under the Seine. At her funeral of September 6, 1997, Diana's sister chose to read the tribute poem to Katrina Trask, the sun-dial poem written by Henry van Dyke in 1901:

> *Hours fly,*
> *Flowers die.*
> *New days,*
> *New ways,*
> *Pass by,*
> *Love stays.*

Time is
Too slow for those who wait,
Too swift for those who fear,
Too long for those who grieve,
Too short for those who rejoice.
But for those who love,
Time is Eternity.[27]

Katrina's influence resurfaced in November 2001 when the same tribute poem was read by actress Judi Dench at Westminster Abbey during a memorial service honoring victims of the September 11th attacks. It has become a permanent part of London's 9/11 memorial at Grosvenor Square Garden.[158]

A *New York Times* editorial on January 9, 1922, noted Katrina Trask was "of another age" living on a stage of expansive gardens and Medieval chivalry, but she was also a lady of practical views who took keen interest in the issues and problems of her time. "She took a tireless, eager part in making things better, whether in her immediate neighborhood or in the wider world."

Later that year, Henry van Dyke gave a eulogy to Katrina at the presentation to the city of Saratoga Springs of a memorial gate in Congress Park:

"She was both an idealist and a realist, a poet and a practical housewife, a dreamer of great dreams and a faithful performer of daily duties. What, then, shall this gateway and these steps, erected by the gifts of the men and women of the estate of Yaddo, say to us of the Lady Katrina, whose

*name they bear? This is what they shall say to every one
who mounts this stairway, who passes through this portal:
Katrina was ever an opener of gates, seeking to show to others the way of entrance into a richer, fuller, finer life."*

After the death of his wife, George Foster Peabody
assumed the task of launching the grand design of his
beloved Trasks. To him fell the responsibility of working
out the financial and practical aspects of opening Yaddo
estate to its first artist residents. By 1923, Foster Peabody had hired a personal assistant, the young Marjorie
Waite, and soon he hired her sister Elizabeth Ames to
survey and catalogue the contents of Yaddo. Elizabeth
Ames so impressed Foster and the board of Yaddo that
some months later she was asked to stay on as the first
Executive Director of the Corporation of Yaddo, making
the house ready for its first creative guests and officially
offering the hospitality.

Between 1924 and 1926 Mrs. Ames established
working relationships with critics, writers, artists, musicians, and editors to help in the selection of residents.
Elizabeth Ames was the perfect director, the voice and
tone of Yaddo. Working with Foster Peabody, Allena
Pardee, and her own sister Marjorie Waite (who became
a resident director) she exercised her duties with great
vision and skill until 1969. Marjorie Waite eventually
was adopted by Foster and would provide the compan-
ionship and communion of mutual interest to sustain
the man left with a special mission by the Trasks.

In 1926 the first artist guests came to Yaddo,
staying for a few weeks, then later for a few months,
assigned to appropriate rooms or outbuildings or stu-

dios on the estate, coming together socially for dinner in the main dining room but keeping the rule of silence and isolation after breakfast. A succession of the most creative individuals of the twentieth century came to Yaddo... artists, composers, film writers, critics, sculptors, poets, novelists... each finding on the estate in the woods freedom from financial restrictions and the necessary solitude and inspiration to create some of their finest masterpieces.

Sometimes among the creative gathering friendships were formed, sometimes collaborations, sometimes disputes, sometimes love affairs. But from the quiet woods of Yaddo would emerge countless awards: 66 Pulitzer prizes; 61 National Book Awards; 40 National Book Critics Circle Awards; some of the finest achievements in film; and a Nobel prize.[159] One frequent guest, John Cheever, wrote that "the forty or so acres on which the principal buildings of Yaddo stand have seen more distinguished activity in the arts than any other piece of ground in the English speaking community and perhaps the world."[160]

Among the resident guests at Yaddo over the decades since its founding are the following cultural icons: Truman Capote, Sylvia Plath, Mario Puzo, Carson McCullers, Katherine Anne Porter, James Baldwin, John Cheever, Langston Hughes, Saul Bellow, Malcolm Cowley, Eudora Welty, Aaron Copland, Leonard Bernstein, Newton Arvin, Irving Stone, Bernard Malamud, Flannery O'Connor, Milton Avery, Patricia Highsmith, Philip Roth, Alice Walker, Jonathan Franzen, and Amy Tan.

The legacy of Katrina and Spencer Trask continues today. In 1940 Triuna Island in Lake George was "sold for $20,000 to support ongoing expenses of hosting artists and writers"[161] at Yaddo, which remains the best known of America's premier artists' retreats.

Wiawaka Holiday House still operates as a peaceful and simple retreat for women on the shores of Lake George. In the beautiful lakeside setting can be found programs for women veterans and for cancer survivors, workshops in the arts, opportunities for rejuvenating the spirit and the body. It is the oldest and longest continuously operational retreat for women in America.

Today the Yaddo archives, "more than five hundred boxes of letters, journals, manuscripts, guest records, photographs, charts, and ephemera dating from 1870 to 1980"[162] have a permanent home at the New York Public Library. They offer a unique view into the cultural history of the twentieth century and also into the personal life of Mrs. Spencer Trask, the Lady of Yaddo.

It is not uncommon for the spirit of Katrina Trask to be felt within the corridors of Yaddo, report some of the artist guests.[163] And *sometimes* from the public gardens below the mansion a fleeting image of a lady in white is seen at the tower window, a lady in white viewing her roses, and then she is gone. ✤

End Notes

Katrina Trask's journals of 1882–1891 were partially and privately printed in 1888 as a eulogy to the Trask children Christina and Spencer Jr. They are referred to here as *The Chronicles of Yaddo 1888*. More inclusive material was printed in 1923 under the direction of Allena Pardee, following instructions of the deceased Katrina Trask, as *Yaddo*, a.k.a. *The Chronicles of Yaddo*, a.k.a. *The Story of Yaddo*. Referred to here as *The Chronicles of Yaddo*.

Also note, some book titles referenced here are abbreviated.   For full titles please consult the *Bibliography*.

1. James G. Blaine was a charismatic nineteenth-century orator, teacher, journalist, and politician who served as Senator, Representative, Secretary of State, and ran unsuccessfully for President against Grover Cleveland in 1884. He was a friend of George Nichols, Kate's father.

2. Christina Trask, as quoted by her mother in *Chronicles of Yaddo 1888*, Yaddo archives held in the New York Public Library.

3. Katrina Trask, *Ibid*.

4. *Ibid*.

5. *Ibid*.

6. Longfellow quoted by Trask in *Chronicles of Yaddo 1888*, Yaddo archives held in the NYPL.

7. Trask, *Ibid*.

8. David S. Worth, *Spencer Trask: Enigmatic Titan*, p. 65.

9. Spencer Trask, as quoted by Katrina in *Chronicles of Yaddo 1888*, Yaddo archives held in the NYPL.

10. Katrina Trask, *Ibid.*

11. *Ibid.*

12. Worth, *Spencer Trask: Enigmatic Titan*, p. 54.

13. Anne Kay Simpson, "The World of Katrina Trask, Lady of Yaddo" research paper written in 1933, p. 45.

14. Marjorie Peabody Waite, *Yaddo: Yesterday and Today*, p. 22.

15. Descriptions of Victorian Saratoga Springs from Hollis Palmer, *See and Be Seen.*

16. Trask, *Chronicles of Yaddo,* Yaddo archives held in the NYPL.

17. *Ibid.*

18. Trask, as related by Waite in *Yaddo: Yesterday and Today*, p. 25.

19. *Ibid.*, p. 26.

20. *Ibid.*

21. Testamentary agreement of Spencer and Katrina Trask, 1899, from the Yaddo archives held in the NYPL.

22. Katrina Trask, as related by Waite in *Yaddo: Yesterday and Today.*

23. *Ibid.*

24. Trask description of her garden in *The Country Calendar,* Dec. 1905. Yaddo archives of the Saratoga Springs Public Library.

25. Waite, *Yaddo: Yesterday and Today*, p. 28.

26. Letter from Foster Peabody to Spencer, from the Yaddo archives held in the NYPL.

27. "For Katrina's Sun-Dial," Henry van Dyke. The poem appears in different sources with the last line as *"Time is Not"* instead of *"Time is Eternity."* This version is from Waite, *Yaddo: Yesterday and Today*, p. 29.

28. Trask description of her garden in *The Country Calendar*, Dec. 1905. Yaddo archives of the Saratoga Springs Public Library.

29. *Ibid.*

30. Junius Trask, as quoted by his mother in *Chronicles of Yaddo 1888,* Yaddo archives held in the NYPL.

31. *Ibid.*

32. Christina Trask, as quoted by her mother in *Chronicles of Yaddo 1888,* Yaddo archives held in the NYPL.

33. *Ibid.*

34. Katrina Trask, *Under King Constantine.* "Sir Christalan, the Valiant and the True."

35. H. Paul Jeffers, *Diamond Jim Brady*, p. 249.

36. *Ibid.*

37. Descriptions of Victorian Saratoga Springs from Palmer, *See and Be Seen.*

38. George Waller, *Saratoga, Saga of an Imperious Era*, p. 228.

39. *Ibid.*, p. 233.

40. *Ibid.*, p. 229.

41. *Ibid.*, p. 254.

42. *Ibid.*, p. 249.

43. General descriptions and anecdotes of Brady from Jeffers, *Diamond Jim Brady.*

44. Worth. *Spencer Trask: Enigmatic Titan*, p. 7.

45. *Ibid*, p. 104.

46. Teri Blasko and Jeff Durstewitz, "Long Ago and Far Away," article on Saratoga Flower Fete at turn of the century, *Mardi Gras Guide 2012.*

47. Louise Ware, *George Foster Peabody*, p. 117.

48. Trask, *Chronicles of Yaddo*, Yaddo archives held in the NYPL.

49. *Ibid.*

50. *Ibid.*

51. *Ibid.*

52. *Ibid.*

53. *Ibid.*

54. Booker T. Washington, *Up From Slavery*, p. 127.

55. *Ibid.*

56. *Ibid.*

57. *Ibid.*, p. 128.

58. *Ibid.*, p. 159.

59. Ware, *George Foster Peabody*, p. 104.

60. *Ibid.*, p. 103.

61. Letter from Helen Keller, correspondence of Katrina Trask, Yaddo archives held in the NYPL.

62. *Ibid.*

63. Episcopal Bishop William Crosswell Doane hoped to create an English cathedral community of church, school, hospital, and convent in Albany. He had founded in that city the St. Agnes School, the Child's Hospital, St. Margaret's House and Hospital for Babies, and had established a community of religious women to work in these institutions. The Trasks entrusted their own St. Christina girls in Saratoga to their direction.

64. Trask, *Chronicles of Yaddo,* Yaddo archives held in the NYPL.

65. Trask, *The Mighty and The Lowly,* p. 24.

66. *Ibid.*

67. See Katrina Trask's novel *Free Not Bound,* 1903.

68. Review of *Under King Constantine, New York Times,* Feb. 18, 1893.

69. See Worth, chapter entitled "Let There Be Light."

70. *Ibid.*, chapter entitled "The Beginning of the Modern Music Industry."

71. *Ibid.*, chapter entitled "The Inspired Choice."

72. *Ibid.*, p. 108.

73. Ware, *George Foster Peabody,* p. 34.

74. Trask papers in Yaddo archives held in the NYPL.

75. Letter from George Foster Peabody in Trask correspondence, Yaddo archives held in the NYPL.

76. Trask, *Chronicles of Yaddo,* Yaddo archives held in the NYPL.

77. Trask, "The Story of Lake George," in the collection of Pat and Dick Swire.

78. Sally V. Svenson, "Past Tents." *Adirondack Life* magazine, 2007.

79. Trask correspondence. Yaddo archives held in the NYPL.

80. Centennial Committee, *A Family of Friends: The First Hundred Years at the Lake George Club, 1909–2009.*

81. Kathryn O'Brien, *The Great and the Gracious*, p. 114.

82. Sally Bixby Defty, *Passionate Pursuits: William Keeney Bixby.*

83. Ware, *George Foster Peabody*, p. 93.

84. Trask, *Chronicles of Yaddo*, Yaddo archives held in the NYPL.

85. Zimmerman, *Love, Fiercely*, p. 188.

86. O'Brien, *The Great and the Gracious*, p. 55.

87. Christina Trask, as quoted by her mother in *Chronicles of Yaddo 1888*, p. 142.

88. *Ibid.*, p. 143.

89. Correspondence, 1906. Yaddo archives held in the NYPL.

90. Simpson, "The World of Katrina Trask...", p. 74.

91. Trask correspondence, Yaddo archives held in the NYPL.

92. *Ibid.*

93. Bishop William Doane, as quoted in Simpson, "The World of Katrina Trask...", p. 76.

94. O'Brien, *The Great and the Gracious*, p. 58.

95. David McCullough, *The Greater Journey: Americans in Paris*, p. 368.

96. *Ibid.*, p. 366.

97. Paul Baker, *Stanny: The Gilded Life of Stanford White*, p. 237.

98. *New York Times*, June 26, 1906.

99. Trask, *Chronicles of Yaddo*, p. 13. Yaddo archives held in the NYPL.

100. *Ibid*.

101. Correspondence found in Yaddo archives held in the NYPL.

102. *Ibid*.

103. Spencer, as quoted by Katrina in *Chronicles of Yaddo*, Yaddo archives held in the NYPL.

104. Trask, "The Story of Lake George."

105. Daniel Vaughan, "1904 Searchmont Touring News, Pictures, and Information." Internet article, Feb. 2007.

106. Waite, *Yaddo: Yesterday and Today*, p. 43.

107. Simpson, "The World of Katrina Trask..."

108. Correspondence of Katrina Trask, Yaddo archives held in the NYPL.

109. Correspondence of Spencer Trask, Yaddo archives held in the NYPL.

110. Correspondence of Katrina Trask, Yaddo archives held in the NYPL.

111. Correspondence of Spencer Trask, Yaddo archives held in the NYPL.

112. Trask, *Chronicles of Yaddo*, Yaddo archives held in the NYPL.

113. Article in the *New York Times*, January 1, 1910.

114. *Ibid*.

115. Dr. Henry van Dyke, quoted in papers found in Yaddo archives held in the NYPL.

116. Rev. Percy Grant, quoted in papers found in Yaddo archives held in the NYPL.

117. Mr. Edward Shepard, quoted in papers found in Yaddo archives held in the NYPL.

118. *Ibid.*

119. Trask papers, Yaddo archives held in the NYPL.

120. Spencer Trask as quoted by Katrina in papers found in Yaddo archives held in the NYPL.

121. *Ibid.*

122. Correspondence of Katrina Trask, Yaddo archives held in the NYPL.

123. *Ibid.*

124. *Ibid.*

125. *Ibid.*

126. Greg King, *A Season of Splendor,* p. 434.

127. *Ibid.*

128. *Ibid.,* p. 438.

129. O'Brien, *The Great and the Gracious,* p. 59

130. Ware, *George Foster Peabody,* p. 156.

131. Peabody, quoted by Ware, p. 167.

132. *Ibid.,* p. 172.

133. Correspondence of George Foster Peabody, Yaddo archives held in the NYPL.

134. Ware, *George Foster Peabody,* p. 181

135. Jean Zimmerman, *Love Fiercely: A Gilded Age Romance,* p. 66.

136. Correspondence of Katrina Trask, Yaddo archives held in the NYPL.

137. Correspondence found in Yaddo archives held in the NYPL.

138. *Ibid.*

139. Correspondence of Katrina Trask, Yaddo archives held in the NYPL.

140. *Ibid.*

141. Trask, "Woman Suffrage a Practical Necessity," essay in *The Woman Citizen,* Oct. 1917.

142. *Ibid.,* p. 368-69

143. Katrina Trask to Adolph Ochs, Feb. 25, 1921. Correspondence found in the Yaddo archives held in the NYPL.

144. *Ibid.*

145. *Ibid.*

146. *Ibid.*

147. *Saratogian* newspaper clipping, Trask papers, Yaddo archives held in the NYPL.

148. *Saratoga Sun,* Saturday, Feb. 5, 1921, newspaper clipping in Katrina's scrapbook, Yaddo archives held in the NYPL.

149. *New York Times,* Sunday, Feb. 6, 1921, newspaper clipping in Katrina's scrapbook, Yaddo archives held in the NYPL.

150. *Saratogian,* Feb. 7, 1921, newspaper clipping in Katrina's scrapbook, Yaddo archives held in the NYPL.

151. *Ibid.*

152. Trask, "Woman Suffrage a Practical Necessity," in *The Woman Citizen*, Oct. 1917.

153. Trask, *Chronicles of Yaddo*, Yaddo archives held in the NYPL.

154. Katrina Trask poem mailed to Mr. and Mrs. Adolph Ochs, Thanksgiving Day, 1918. Yaddo archives held in the NYPL.

155. Katrina's words on her garden in *The Country Calendar* magazine, December 1905. Yaddo archives of the Saratoga Springs Public Library.

156. *Ibid.*

157. Christina Trask, as quoted by her mother in *Chronicles of Yaddo 1888*, Yaddo archives held in the NYPL.

158. Several Internet websites including those of London *Daily Mail* (*Mail Online*); and *Voices of September 11th*.

159. Corporation of Yaddo Internet website.

160. Comments of John Cheever to the board of the Corporation of Yaddo, Sept. 7, 1968. Yaddo archives held in the NYPL.

161. See Yaddo Timeline, *Yaddo: Making American Culture*, p. 125.

162. Preface of *Yaddo: Making American Culture*.

163. Allan Gurganus, "The Ghosts of Yaddo," in Micki McGee, *Yaddo: Making American Culture*.

Bibliography

Baker, Paul R. *Stanny: The Gilded Life of Stanford White.* The Free Press, a division of Macmillan, Inc., New York, 1989.

Defty, Sally Bixby. *Passionate Pursuits: William Keeney Bixby,* Bolton Landing, N.Y., 2012.

Gates, William Preston. *Millionaires' Row on Lake George, NY.* W. P. Gates Publishing Co., Queensbury, N.Y., 2008.

Jeffers, H. Paul. *Diamond Jim Brady: Prince of the Gilded Age.* John Wiley and Sons, New York, Chichester, Weinheim, Brisbane, Singapore, Toronto, 2001.

Kaplan, Justin. *When the Astors Owned New York.* A Plume Book, Penguin Group, New York, 2007.

King, Greg. *A Season of Splendor: The Court of Mrs. Astor in Gilded Age New York.* John Wiley & Sons, Inc., Hoboken, N. J., 2009.

McGee, Micki. *Yaddo: Making American Culture.* New York Public Library and Columbia University Press, New York, 2008.

McCullough, David M. *The Greater Journey: Americans in Paris 1830-1900.* Simon and Schuster, New York, London, Toronto, Sydney, 2011.

O'Brien, Kathryn E. *The Great and the Gracious on Millionaires' Row: Lake George in its Glory.* North Country Books, Sylvan Beach, N.Y., 1978.

Palmer, Hollis. *See and Be Seen: Saratoga in the Victorian Era.* Deep Roots Publications, Saratoga Springs, N.Y., 2010.

Parker, Richard K. *The Trask Chronicles: A Digest of Writings About Spencer and Katrina Trask*. Self published, Lock Haven, Penn., 2009.

Peabody, Marjorie Waite. *Yaddo: Yesterday and Today*. Argus Press, Albany, N.Y., 1933. Reprinted 1999.

Riis, Jacob A. *How the Other Half Lives*. Charles Scribner's Sons, New York, 1890.

Simpson, Anne Kay. "The World of Katrina Trask, Lady of Yaddo," research paper. Lafayette, La. Written 1933; copyright 1995.

Stuart, Amanda Mackenzie. *Consuelo and Alva Vanderbilt: The story of a daughter and a mother in the Gilded Age*. Harper Collins Publishers, Great Britain, 2005.

Svenson, Sally V. "Past Tents," *Adirondack Life*, Jay, N.Y., Special Collectors Issue 2007.

Trask, Katrina. *The Chronicles of Yaddo*. Private journal, 1882–1891. Printed under the direction of Allena Pardee following instructions of the deceased Katrina Trask, as *Yaddo*, a.k.a. *The Chronicles of Yaddo*, a.k.a. *The Story of Yaddo*. In Saratoga Springs, N.Y., 1923.

Trask, Katrina. *The Chronicles of Yaddo 1888*. Partial printing of Katrina Trask journals; a eulogy to the Trask children Christina and Spencer Jr. Privately printed, 1888.

Trask, Katrina. *Free Not Bound*. G. P. Putnam's Sons, New York and London, 1903. Digitally remastered by Forgotten Books, Lexington, Ky., 2012.

Trask, Katrina. *In the Vanguard*. Macmillan Co., New York, 1913.

Trask, Katrina. *The Mighty and the Lowly*. Macmillan Co., New York, 1915. Reprinted by New York Public Library.

Trask, Katrina. "The Story of Lake George," n. d. Type script pages in the collection of Pat and Dick Swire.

Trask, Katrina. *Under King Constantine*. Third Edition, 1893. Reprint, Kessinger Publishing, Great Britain, 2012.

Trask, Katrina. "Woman Suffrage a Practical Necessity," *The Woman Citizen* (1:20), New York, Oct. 13, 1917.

Waller, George. *Saratoga: Saga Of An Imperious Era*. Bonanza Books, New York, 1966.

Ware, Louise. *George Foster Peabody: Banker, Philanthropist, Publicist*. University of Georgia Press, Athens, Ga., 1951.

Washington, Booker T. *Up From Slavery*. Doubleday Page and Co., New York, 1901. Reprint, Oxford University Press, USA, 2000.

Worth, David S. *Spencer Trask: Enigmatic Titan*. Kabique, Inc., New York, 2008.

Zimmerman, Jean. *Love Fiercely: A Gilded Age Romance*. Houghton Mifflin Harcourt, Boston, New York, 2012.

Internet Sources

Corporation of Yaddo. Found at < http://yaddo.org/yaddo/home.asp >

van Dyke, Henry. "Katrina's Sun-Dial", ca. 1899. Reference to use of poem at Sept. 11 [2001] memorial services found at:

> *Voices of September 11th* < http://voicesofseptember11.org/dev/memorials.php?mem_id=159 >

> *Mail Online*, site for the London *Daily Mail* newspaper < http://www.dailymail.co.uk/news/article-195747/Memorial-garden-9-11-victims.html >

> *Anglo-American Experience* blog of M. E. Foley < http://mefoley.wordpress.com/2011/09/20/911-garden/ >

Vaughn, Daniel. "1904 Searchmont touring news, pictures, and information." Feb. 2007. Found at < http://www.conceptcarz.com/vehicle/z13233/Searchmont-Touring.aspx >

About the Author

Lynn Esmay is a former teacher of English and
social studies in private schools in Dallas, Texas,
Newport, Rhode Island, and Charleston, South
Carolina. She holds a BA degree in English from
Sweet Briar College, and an MA degree in history
from Southern Methodist University. Lynn lives
in Naples, Florida, and spends summers with her
husband on Lake George in the Adirondacks.
This is a debut novel. ❧